BINARY

ISBN 979-8-9887078-0-6 *Paperback*
979-8-9887078-1-3 *Hardcover*
979-8-9887078-2-0 *Ebook*

Book cover by Zachary Elliott.
Editing by Cynthia Breheny.
Formatting by Paradox Press.

Printed by Amazon Kindle Direct Publishing.
First Edition, 2023.

Published by Paradox Press.
www.theparadoxinstitute.com

BINARY

DEBUNKING THE SEX SPECTRUM MYTH

ZACHARY ELLIOTT

PARADOX PRESS
THEPARADOXINSTITUTE.COM

To those who never give up the search for truth about our natural world wherever it may be found.

CONTENTS

INTRODUCTION

A NEW PSEUDOSCIENCE

••

There is a new pseudoscience emerging that denies the biological reality of male and female. It's called the **sex spectrum**. Unlike other pseudoscience such as astrology, creationism, or the flat earth, this belief system has garnered mainstream appeal from social theorists, academics, and even biomedical scientists.

Scientific journals like *Nature* have argued that the male and female sexes, the very roles required for us to reproduce as a species, are overly simplistic, and that sex exists on a spectrum rather than a binary of male and female. Other theorists have argued that male and female are not real categories but completely constructed by society. And some science magazines like *Scientific American* have even argued that the idea of two sexes is a "myth" originating in the 1800s. Some of those who are redefining sex do so out of a belief they are creating a more inclusive environment for people with atypical bodies, psychologies, orientations, or identities. Others do so out of a broader sociopolitical agenda to redefine the sexes according to subjective identity.

But accepting those who are different does not require a rejection of male and female and our sexed bodies. In fact, male and female form the bedrock for the sexual diversity in our bodies and our behavior. Furthermore, if the sexes did not exist, then none of us would exist as we know it, since we each originate from the combined genomes of a male (our father) and a female (our mother).

With sex spectrum pseudoscience invading our institutions, many scientists are now countering the concerning denial of male and female. One group of biologists, writing in the peer-reviewed journal BioEssays, directly responded to such claims in 2022:

> The rejection of biological sex seems to be based on a lack of knowledge about evolution and it champions species chauvinism, inasmuch as it imposes human identity notions on millions of other species. We argue that the biological definition of the sexes remains central to recognizing the diversity of life ... Denying the concept of biological sex, for whatever cause, ultimately erodes scientific progress and may open the flood gates to 'alternative truths.'[1]

For this book, we combat the pseudoscience of sex. Each chapter deconstructs a popular sex spectrum argument published in social media, a science magazine, or a peer-reviewed journal. Our scientific claims come directly from biology literature, such as textbooks and scientific studies. Like other pseudoscience, the sex spectrum misuses scientific knowledge to make its arguments seem robust, and so we will analyze the biological literature they misuse and show how it reinforces the sexual system of male and female.

In the beginning chapter, we summarize the sex spectrum belief system, show how each claim is missing crucial connections to biology, and reveal how biology elegantly and consistently defines the sexes. The remaining chapters refute a popular sex spectrum argument by analyzing their false claims with biological knowledge.

---

1 Goymann, W., Brumm, H., Kappeler, P. (2022). Biological sex is binary, even though there is a rainbow of sex roles. *BioEssays, 45(2).*

OVERVIEW

WHAT IS THE "SEX SPECTRUM"?

The male and female sexes are ancient. Having evolved from simpler sexually reproducing ancestors, the sexes emerged on the evolutionary landscape more than one billion years ago.[1] This is older than humans, older than most plant and animal species, older than most marine life, and even older than the brain itself.[2] This means they are some of the most primal systems that exist on our planet.

More than just keeping an individual alive like food and water do, the two sexes keep entire species alive by producing more genetically unique individuals through sexual reproduction: the mixing of genomes and the fusion of sex cells called gametes, and along with it, genetic diversity. The evolution of male and female sexes is a major reason why the diversity of plant and animal species exists. It's why we as humans exist. It's why *you* exist.

Since the evolution of the two sexes, more than 99.9% of animal species reproduce sexually.[3] And 95% of those animal species have male and female sexes in separate individuals,[4] where organisms are either male or female for their entire lives.[5] This is the same sexual system in humans, and it is a major source of biodiversity across the plant and animal kingdoms.[6]

It may be surprising, but the two sexes have a universal biological definition that applies to all species with male and female systems: the male sex is the phenotype (or structure) that produces the smaller gametes (sperm), and the female sex is the phenotype (or structure) that produces the larger gametes (eggs).[7] The sperm are numerous and fast, contributing half the genetic material of the parent but no resources for the zygote's survival. The eggs are voluminous, few, and very slow, contributing half the genetic material of the parent and all the resources for the zygote's survival.[8] Combine these two different gamete types together and a genetically unique individual is formed.

The technical term for this system is known as *anisogamy* (aniso = unequal, and gamy = marriage), which involves the fusion of two gametes with different size and form.[9] It is so efficient for reproduction and producing genetic diversity that it has evolved independently in nearly all lineages of multicellular organisms.[10]

Biologists consider the evolution of the two sexes *mathematically inevitable* because it maximizes the efficiency of sexual reproduction, providing resources to the offspring through investment in large, nutrient heavy eggs, while also maximizing gamete fusion through the production of many sperm that are not as resource intensive and yet can quickly search for and find the egg.[11] This efficiency is why it has evolved independently so many times.

Since the origins of the sexes, male and female have developed specialized reproductive anatomies for producing and releasing sperm and eggs. Sometimes species combine these anatomies into one individual, where an organism is both male and female at the same time, and therefore, can produce both gamete types (a type of male-female system known as *hermaphroditism*).[12] Mammals, however, separate these anatomies, where individuals are either male or female through their entire lives, and therefore, can produce only one gamete type, not both (a type of male-female system known as *gonochorism*).[13]

Like humans, most species with male and female sexes have gonads (testes or ovaries). Testes are the factories for sperm, and ovaries are the factories for eggs. Along with the gonads, they also have genitalia to transport or receive these gametes so they can meet and fuse with each other. The gonads and the genitalia form the reproductive system.

This is how we identify sex in individual organisms: we observe the set of structures that produce and release either gamete type (the sexual phenotype). While the reproductive anatomies can be widely diverse in appearance across species, the sexes are always defined the same: the two different roles in reproduction, differentiated by gamete type.[14]

Yet these undeniable evolutionary facts have not escaped the deconstruction tools of theorists and activists who seek to subvert and redefine the meaning of male and female for social and political purposes. One attractive belief has gained mainstream prominence across academic, social, and political institutions, making people reject the idea that male and female are objective, biological realities.[15] [16] [17] [18]

This belief system is known as the *sex spectrum*: the idea that 1) sex exists on a continuum, 2) male and female are socially constructed, and 3) one's internal sense of self is the most accurate parameter for sex.

Many proponents of the sex spectrum are driven by the idea that the two sexes are constructed categories, created by society, to oppress and control sexual minorities. Some know that male and female are real, ancient realities yet argue against them out of a sense of compassion to those who insist on denying them. Others believe that male and female do not capture the full reality of human experience, arguing that individuals exist on a continuum of traits between male and female.

Proponents of the sex spectrum have diverse backgrounds: parents and teachers, social activists and academics, and politicians and lawmakers. Though they all have different reasons for arguing that male and female are not real, they each align in the belief that male and female must be superseded by a subjective, feeling-based reality, where one's internal sense of self is prioritized over the truthful and important reality of our sexed bodies.

Because of the appeals to compassion or to scientific knowledge, the sex spectrum has become one of the most dominant ideas in the controversial sex and gender debates. It is so popular in fact that mainstream science journals like *Nature* have published pieces claiming that "the idea of two sexes is simplistic."[19] And science magazines like the

famous *Scientific American* have argued that the male and female sexes are not real at all but "myths" originating in the 1800s.[20] This phenomenon is not new at all. It has been brewing in sociology for decades, and its history stretches back over a hundred years. It's just been repackaged under new branding.

For our purposes, this new pseudoscience of sex can be traced back to the last decade of the 20th century, when the male-female system was met with an explosion of critiques from the field of Sociology of Gender. The landmark Sociology of Gender textbook, *Questioning Gender: A Sociological Exploration*, represents this view, where professor of sociology Robyn Ryle explores how sex, not just gender, is socially constructed. Ryle writes:

> Sex categories are socially constructed...there are not two kinds of distinguishable male and female bodies in the world.[21]

It is not that all theorists believe physical bodies themselves are socially constructed (though some do). Rather, sex spectrum pseudoscientists believe that the line dividing male bodies from female bodies is culturally and temporally defined. In other words, the criteria dividing male from female is thought to be determined by place and time, not biology.

Most of the contemporary theorists and activists in Sociology of Gender believe that male and female are wholly socially constructed and that no criteria can reliably differentiate the two. Professor Ryle refers to this concept as strong social constructionism:

> Strong social constructionism (SSC): There are no criteria that will consistently and reliably sort people into the categories of male and female.

Building upon academic theory from Sociology of Gender, the argument that biological sex exists on a continuum and that male and female are socially constructed applies three major principles: first, a

biological one; second, a social one; and third, a political one. We are going to critically analyze these three major principles to understand the components of the sex spectrum argument, and you will see these principles show up many times throughout the book.

SEX SPECTRUM BIOLOGICAL PRINCIPLE

Sex exists on a continuum between male and female.

SEX SPECTRUM SOCIAL PRINCIPLE

There are no criteria that will reliably sort people into male and female categories. Therefore, male and female are socially constructed.

SEX SPECTRUM POLITICAL PRINCIPLE

One's internal sense of whether one is male, female, both, or neither (also known as gender identity) determines sex.

These three principles—biological, social, and political—are the core of the sex spectrum argument. In writings by theorists, activists, scientists, journalists, and politicians, the three-step sequence will often be presented in order, beginning with the biological, moving to the social, and ending with the political.

The biological principle represents the scientific shield of the sex spectrum because it serves as an effective defense for the social and political agendas behind it. It works as a deconstructive tool by using various sleight-of-hand tricks, with scientific language, to destabilize a person's understanding of sex and the two sexes.

Once one's understanding of male and female has been destabilized, the social principle acts as the bridge between the biological and political—that, in the view of the theorists, male and female are arbitrary social constructs which cannot be consistently defined.

Finally, the political principle lays out the real-world application of the sex spectrum argument—that because male and female are socially

constructed, one's internal sense of self is the most reasonable parameter for sex in most, if not all, spheres of life. This principle is then used to redefine male and female around subjective identity, replacing the definition of sex with one's internal sense of self—most often referred to as gender identity.

For example, the New York City Commission on Human Rights defines gender identity as the "primary determinant of a person's sex."[22] The political principle of the sex spectrum is the most insidious because, when used by activists and politicians who do not balance the legal protections for sex, it can quickly be used to erode the rights and safety of males and females alike.

Now that we have a base understanding, let's analyze the three principles in detail and debunk their fundamental claims.

SEX SPECTRUM BIOLOGICAL PRINCIPLE

Sex exists on a continuum between male and female.

The biological principle appropriates a wide range of scientific information from evolutionary and developmental biology, from medical conditions in humans to sex determination mechanisms and sex characteristics in other animals. Throughout its claims, this principle misrepresents scientific literature on the two sexes by applying four argument strategies.

1. *Define sex as a mix of traits detached from reproduction.*
2. *Use medical conditions as exceptions to male and female.*
3. *Conflate sex determination mechanisms with sex.*
4. *Conflate sex characteristics with sex.*

The first strategy—*define sex as a mix of traits detached from reproduction*—is the foundation for the sex spectrum. Detaching sex from its evolved function (reproduction) and constructing a definition around the variation in people's bodies (such as chromosomes, gonads,

genitalia, hormones, facial hair, breasts, etc.) allows proponents of the sex spectrum to construct their main argument: *variation challenges the two sexes.*

The second strategy—*use medical conditions as exceptions to male and female*—is one of the most common techniques employed by sex spectrum proponents. The theorists and activists do this because they see people with these medical conditions as subversive identities (exceptions) to the male-female dyad who can then be used as deconstructive tools, like pawns on a chessboard, to further their own social and political goals.[23]

The third strategy—*conflate sex determination mechanisms with sex*—uses the diversity of sex determination mechanisms in other animals and conflates them with sex. This is supposed to prove that male and female are socially constructed categories. Animals across the diversity of life have very different mechanisms for developing sex in individuals. For example, mammals tend to use an X-Y chromosomal system, birds tend to use Z-W, and other species do not use sex chromosomes at all. Because of this diversity, sex spectrum proponents conclude that sex exists on a continuum, and that male and female are socially constructed.

Finally, the fourth strategy—*conflate sex characteristics with sex*—uses species across the diversity of life with widely different and incredibly fascinating anatomies, physiologies, and behaviors. This diversity is used to argue that male and female cannot be reliably defined.

1. *Define sex as a mix of traits detached from reproduction.*

To dismantle the sexes, proponents will first define sex according to a mix of traits—kind of like a Mr. Potato Head style mishmash of traits. In the sex spectrum, sex is not defined as the phenotypes that produce two differently sized gametes, but as a continuum of chromosomes, gonads, genitals, and hormones—all of which can vary to infinite degrees. According to the sex spectrum, male and female are clusters of specific traits, and those who do not have the correct clusters are neither male nor female. Proponents claim these clusters form two averages, or peaks, in a bimodal distribution (a range of data with two modes, or two clusters of data). Males represent one peak, and females represent another peak, while people in between the "peaks" of male and female are "intersex."

This constructed definition of male and female has a major consequence: anyone who falls outside these clusters of traits is no longer a male or female but rather more male or less male, more female or less female, both or neither. For example, in the sex spectrum, males with smaller penises are considered less male than males with longer penises, whereas females with larger breasts and wider hips would be more female than females with a larger clitoris and smaller breasts. This logic is even applied to chromosomal disorders, where males with an extra X chromosome are considered "less male" and males with an extra Y are considered "more male" even though these extra chromosomes do not make these males any "more" or "less" male.

Once you understand this—that the sex spectrum categorizes people according to a stereotyped and arbitrary ideal of "what bodies look like"—the various problems with it become obvious. Thus, the sex spectrum is purely descriptive at best without any understanding of what reproductive function these interconnected traits serve.[24]

Male and female are not a mix of traits but rather two distinct phenotypes that produce two different gamete types.[25] Defining them as a mix of traits that can all vary independently ignores the evolutionary function of the sexes and the science of sex differentiation and development.[26] The function of the sexes is to produce two differently sized gametes to combine so that new individuals can be produced. The gonads, genitals, and hormones work together to support this function.

This cannot be mixed and matched because these traits develop in a sequential, hierarchical order. In other words, each trait builds on the other. The chromosomes have genes which determine the development of the gonads (the gamete factories), and the gonads secrete hormones which help build the internal and external genitalia (the transportation systems for the gametes).[27]

The reason why there are two averages in the distribution when sex differences are plotted together is because there are only two groups being compared: the two sexes. One distribution shows variation in anatomy, physiology, and behavior within males, and the other distribution shows variation in anatomy, physiology, and behavior within females.[28] For instance, height differences between the sexes can be considered bimodal, and they overlap significantly. Yet this does not mean that sex itself is bimodal, or that short males are suddenly "less male" or that tall females are suddenly "less female." There is one distribution of height for males, and one distribution for females, and where the distributions overlap is where the sexes have traits in common.

Arguing that male and female cannot be defined because they share traits in common would be like arguing that apples and oranges cannot be defined because they too share traits in common. But trait overlap between two categories does not always mean that the categories are completely constructed by society.

While variation in sex-related traits is common, this variation exists within the evolved male-female system. Across all species that reproduce through anisogamy, male and female are defined according to the phenotype they develop with respect to either sperm or eggs. As sex difference researcher Marco Del Guidice writes:

> The biological definition of sex is not just one option among many equally valid alternatives; the very existence of differentiated males and females in a species depends on the existence of two gamete types.[29]

Finally, sex spectrum proponents fail to define the axes of their "spectrum of sex." Measurable units are never given, nor is it explained how exactly an individual can be accurately plotted on the distribution. All data sets must be defined with units, or else they cannot be plotted. But because the sex spectrum fails to provide a model (or even consistent logic) for how individuals can be predictably placed on such a spectrum, it fails basic scientific standards. This is because the sex spectrum defines sex as a mix of independent traits and detaches these traits (like gonads and genitalia) from their evolved reproductive functions. In doing so, it fails to understand how these systems are tightly dependent on the other.

2. *Use medical conditions as exceptions to male and female.*

After detaching sex from reproduction, theorists and activists will then use medical conditions that negatively impact the development of male and female reproductive systems, known as disorders of sex development. Because these disorders do not always fit their narrow "cluster of traits" definition for the sexes, they claim such conditions are exceptions to male and female.

For example, proponents of the sex spectrum will often point to chromosomal conditions such as XO, XXX, XXY, and XXXY as additional sexes.[30] But when we return to the biological definition of sex, all such conditions collapse into two simple outcomes: males and females. Those with XO and XXX chromosomes develop the phenotype that produces large gametes (they are females),[31] and those with XXY and XXXY develop the phenotype that produces small gametes (they are males).[32] This is due to the genes within the chromosomes, which control the development path.[33] Genes like SRY, the sex-determining region on the Y chromosome, develops fetuses into males, whereas genes like WNT4 and RSPO1 develop fetuses into females.[34] Therefore, such atypical chromosome combinations are not examples of additional sexes nor are they exceptions to male and female categories; they are developmental disorders within the two categories.[35]

Other disorders of sex development result in a sex opposite of what is expected from the chromosomes, such as an XX male or an XY female. This occurs due to gene translocations or mutations. For example, when the SRY gene translocates onto an X chromosome in an XX zygote, the fetus will develop testes and a penis. This results in a male despite the absence of the Y chromosome.[36]

Other disorders result in under-masculinization of genitalia in males (smaller penis and testes) or over-masculinization in females (larger clitoris and fusion of the labia).[37] Yet each one of these developmental disorders, when understood within the biological definition of sex, are not exceptions to male and female; rather, they are genetic disorders within males and within females.

3. *Conflate sex determination mechanisms with sex.*

The third strategy often employed in the sex spectrum biological principle utilizes the diversity of sex determination mechanisms in other species to argue that male and female are unreliable categories.

Sex determination mechanisms are the regulatory systems, genetic and environmental, that determine the development path the organism will take for their sex.[38] Proponents of the sex spectrum are correct that sex determination mechanisms are widely varied across species. But they are incorrect this somehow invalidates the categories of male and female in humans.

In fact, it is ironically the inverse: the diversity of sex determination mechanisms across species solidifies the biological categories of male and female in humans. While there is a wide diversity of sex determination mechanisms across anisogamous species, all these mechanisms result in the production of males and females.[39] As geneticist Leo Beukeboom and evolutionary ecologist Nicolas Perrin write in their book, *The Evolution of Sex Determination*:

> Among the many surprises and oddities that biological investigations on sexes are revealing, one is particularly intriguing: even in higher eukaryotes with well-differentiated male and female roles, the initial steps of sex-determination pathways are bewilderingly diverse and extraordinarily labile. Evolutionary biolo-

> gists seek to understand this conundrum: what might drive the surprising dynamics of such a fundamental process that, at the end, always leads to the same and simple outcome: the production of males and females?

In other words, while there is a wide diversity of mechanisms that develop an organism's sex across species, the outcome is the same: production of males and females. For example, unlike humans, who have a chromosomal sex determination system of X-Y, birds have a chromosomal sex determination system of Z-W. Eggs with ZZ develop as males, whereas eggs with ZW develop as females. We can only recognize that ZZ birds are male and ZW birds are female if we already understand what male and female are.

Other sex determination systems do not use chromosomes at all. For example, in crocodiles, sex is determined by environmental temperature, a process known as temperature sex determination (TSD). Crocodile eggs incubated at around 34 degrees Celsius and above develop as males, whereas eggs at temperatures around 30 degrees Celsius develop as females.[40] From this range of temperatures, we would not say that sex in crocodiles exists on a spectrum. Rather, the range of temperatures at which sex will be determined exists on a spectrum. The resultant sex is either male or female.

If sex determination mechanisms were biological sex, then species that determine sex by a range of temperatures would have infinite sexes. Each temperature value would be a distinct sex just as every possible chromosome combination in humans would be a distinct sex.

Developmental biologist Dr. Emma Hilton explains the absurdity of this false claim:

> By understanding that a range of determination temperatures can all lead to the same sex in crocodiles, one can then make parallels with different chromosome configurations leading to the same sex in humans. If we flip the argument so that different determination

> conditions define different sexes—an XY person is a different sex to an XXY person—we must carry that through to crocodiles. It would be dishonest to argue the premise for only humans. And effectively, because temperature is divisible into very small categories indeed, we end up with infinite crocodile sexes. They are named: 20.000001, 20.000002, 20.000003, etc.[41]

The fact that sex determination mechanisms across anisogamous species are so diverse while consistently and reliably producing males and females, not something else or in-between, is a direct refutation of the argument that sex determination mechanisms prove sex exists on a continuum or that male and female are socially constructed. Confusing sex determination mechanisms for sex is like confusing the various ingredients of a cake for the cake itself.

4. *Conflate sex characteristics with sex.*

The fourth major strategy of the sex spectrum's biological principle conflates the diversity of sex characteristics within humans and between species with a continuum of sexes. Sex characteristics—both primary ones such as gonads (testes or ovaries) and secondary ones such as facial hair or breasts—are the physical traits that are associated with the organism's reproductive role as a male or female.

Let's first look at an easy example: the diversity of breasts and facial hair in humans. There is a spectrum of breast size and shape in humans, but this does not mean sex itself is a spectrum. Breasts are identified as a 'female' trait precisely because they most often occur with the large gamete phenotype. If a male grows breast tissue due to a genetic disorder, he is not suddenly less male or closer to being a female. He retains his reproductive role as a male regardless of the growth in breast tissue. Likewise, there is a spectrum of facial hair in humans, but this does not mean sex itself is a spectrum. Facial hair is often identified as a 'male' trait precisely because it occurs most often in the small gamete phenotype. If a female grows facial hair, she is not suddenly less female or closer to being a male. She retains her reproductive role as a female regardless of the growth in facial hair. Sex characteristics like breasts and facial hair are traits that are associated with the sexes of male or female, but they do not define the sexes.

Another example involves primary sex characteristics such as testes and ovaries. While testes and ovaries are the organs that produce gametes and are therefore inextricably linked to sex, these organs are not sexes. They are structures that support the reproductive roles of male and female. If testes and ovaries were sexes, then we could not categorize the sex of organisms in other species who do not have testes or ovaries and yet produce small or large gametes regardless, such as the brown alga Ectocarpus, which produces male and female gametes but does not have gonads like animals.[42]

If the sexes are to retain their biological meaning across species, they cannot be defined by appearance of sex characteristics; they must be defined according to the role they play in reproduction: the two different gamete contributions. Sex characteristics evolved from the origins of the two distinct reproductive roles.[43] They are products of the evolution of the two sexes; they are not sexes themselves.[44]

After conflating the diversity of sex characteristics in humans with there being a continuum of sexes, theorists and activists will also use the diversity of sex characteristics in other species to destabilize your understanding of male and female so that they can persuade you to agree with their social and political goals. Common examples used by sex spectrum proponents are hyenas, clownfish, seahorses, slugs, flowering plants, fungi, and other intriguing sexually reproducing species. Let's explore them.

First, the hyena. Hyenas have only two sexes, male and female, but they also have unique sex characteristics that at first glance seem to contradict the understanding of sex in humans. Specifically, the female hyena does not have an external vaginal opening but rather an external structure that looks like a penis. In fact, the hyena is the only mammalian species to lack an external vaginal opening.[45] Because of this, proponents of the sex spectrum will argue that the sex characteristics of the female hyena are evidence the divisions between male and female are arbitrary. However, this is far from the case. The penis-like structure on the female hyena is not a penis. It is a massive clitoris with a central canal through which the female urinates, copulates, and gives birth.[46] When we return to the biological definition of sex, we can see she is a female because she has the phenotype that produces eggs. Thus, the female hyena is not an exception to the male-female dyad but rather just another example of the profound diversity within the two sexes.

Clownfish have only two sexes, male and female, just like humans, and yet unlike humans, they are sequential hermaphrodites: they change sex based on environmental context (from male to female).[47] [48] In this process, not only do their surface level sex characteristics change, but their entire reproductive role changes. The testes become ovaries, and they go from producing sperm to producing ova.[49] Sex spectrum proponents will often use clownfish to show that male and female are socially constructed, traversable categories. And yet at any moment, we know which ones are male and which are female based on whether they have the phenotype that produces sperm or the phenotype that produces eggs, just like humans. And unlike clownfish, humans cannot change sex. Regardless, the sexes in both humans and clownfish are anything but socially constructed.

Seahorses have only two sexes, male and female, in separate individuals. Though they are not sequential hermaphrodites like clownfish, they have a unique form of sex: the males carry the developing babies, a trait usually found in mammalian females. During reproduction, the female seahorse deposits thousands of eggs in the male's brood pouch, which the male then fertilizes. For the next few weeks, the male carries the babies before they are released from his pouch. He even provides them with prolactin, the same hormone that produces milk in pregnant mammals.[50] Sex spectrum proponents may use male seahorses as an example to show the supposed constructed nature of how we define male and female. After all, males in some species can carry babies! And yet the male seahorse is defined as male precisely because they share a unifying trait with all other males across species: the phenotype that produces sperm. Therefore, they are male in the same way that male humans are male. They are not exceptions to the two sexes but within-sex variations.

Slugs have only two sexes, male and female, but most slug species are simultaneous hermaphrodites. This means that they have both male and female sexes in the same individual, and therefore, they can produce both gametes and fertilize themselves.[51]

Theorists and activists, and even some famous authors such as Margaret Atwood, have used the strange world of 'slug sex' as a supposed refutation of the male-female dyad: "Those stuck on Nature being immutably divided into M+F should delve into slug sex."[52] Yet these slimy hermaphrodites only reinforce the biological foundation of male and female. They only have two sexes: their phenotype produces both sperm (male) and eggs (female). Thus, they are an example of how the dual system of sex can be composed in other species.

Flowering plants are also used by theorists and activists as supposed exceptions to the two sexes. But all plants that reproduce through the fusion of two gametes of differing size (anisogamy) simply represent the variation within the dual system of sex. Some of them have male and female flowers on the same plant, and others have flowers that are all male or all female.[53] Female flowers produce the eggs, and male flowers produce the sperm. Thus, like all other forms of anisogamous sexual reproduction where there are only two sexes, flowering plants are simply variations within males and females. They do not show that sex exists on a continuum or that it is socially constructed. They simply reinforce the system of male and female.

Proponents of the sex spectrum often claim that humans can be hermaphrodites, but this is not the case. Humans, like all other mammals, are a gonochoric species.[54] This means that individuals are either male or female through their entire life cycle (like dioecy in plants). In mammals, the genetic and hormonal mechanisms that regulate sex development are mutually antagonistic—as one reproductive system develops, it inhibits the other from developing.[55 56 57]

In humans, if the gonads differentiate into testes during fetal development, they release two hormones: anti-Müllerian hormone and testosterone. Anti-Müllerian hormone disintegrates the vestigial female structures, and the testosterone builds the male structures (in other words, as the male system develops, it inhibits the development of the female system, and vice-versa).[58] Found most often in species with genetic sex determination, this mutually antagonistic system explains why there are no human hermaphrodites.

While individuals can have vestigial remnants of the opposite-sex reproductive system caused by genetic mutations—such as a male developing with a partial uterus, or a female with a mix of internal ovarian and testicular tissue—both male and female reproductive roles cannot fully develop and function in the same individual. As predicted from evolutionary and developmental biology, there has been no documented case of a human having both fully developed reproductive systems in the same individual.[59] If there were such cases, or some are shown in the future, this would mean that it is possible for a human to fulfill both reproductive roles at the same time, and thus, such an individual would be male and female at the same time—a simultaneous hermaphrodite. This would be an example of how the two sexes can be composed in an individual, but not evidence against the existence of male and female.

Finally, when all else fails, theorists and activists will point to species that do not have male and female sexes. For example, sex spectrum proponents will point to various types of organisms that reproduce through gametes of the same size, a form of sexual reproduction known as isogamy (iso = same, gamy = marriage).[60] Isogamy is most common among simpler organisms like algae or fungi. It occurs when all gametes are morphologically similar, particularly in size, and when the contribution of genetic material and resources to the offspring is shared equally between the two parents. This differs from anisogamy (male-female sex) because, in anisogamy, the two gametes (the sperm and egg) are morphologically different in size and the contribution of resources to the offspring are highly unequal.

Proponents of the sex spectrum claim that isogamous organisms can have tens of thousands of sexes. But this conflates mating types with sexes. Mating types involve isogamy (same size gametes), and sexes involve anisogamy (different size gametes). Mating types are molecular mechanisms that regulate compatibility between gametes.[61] Isogamous organisms like fungi can have thousands of pairs of these complementary gamete genotypes (thousands of unique pairs of locks and keys), and therefore, they can have thousands of mating types, but not sexes.[62] Using fungi that do not reproduce through anisogamy as evidence against male and female is an obvious red herring. The only response required to such a tactic is this: humans are not fungi.

Whether it is humans, hyenas, clownfish, seahorses, flowering plants, slugs, or other kinds of anisogamous species, the sexes are defined the same: two roles organized around the production of two gametes of differing size and form. As evolutionary biologists Jussi Lehtonen and Geoff Parker write:

> Of course, in many species a whole suite of secondary sexual traits exists, but the fundamental definition is rooted in this difference in gametes, and the question of the origin of the two sexes is then equal to the question of why do gametes come in two different sizes.[63]

SEX SPECTRUM SOCIAL PRINCIPLE

There are no criteria that will reliably sort people into male and female categories. Therefore, male and female are socially constructed.

Once you believe the biological principle, the social principle is more effective at convincing you that male and female are arbitrary, socially constructed classifications. It does this by using the complex biological variation among individuals and showing some traits for identifying sex can conflict with one another in rare developmental disorders. This is known as the *univariate fallacy*: for two categories to exist, there must be a single trait that differentiates them.[64]

In complex systems, one single trait is often not enough to always differentiate two categories. Multiple variables are needed. For example, it is near impossible to differentiate the faces of human males and human females with one single trait. But when the full range of traits are analyzed together, male and female faces can be distinguished with near 100% accuracy.[65] The same principle applies to the brain.[66] [67] Thus, with a multivariate analysis, two categories can often be consistently and reliably distinguished.[68]

Identifying the sex of a human, however, is far easier than identifying male and female faces. In fact, external genitalia alone is an accurate marker of male or female sex in 99.98% of births.[69] Further, karyotype, one's collection of chromosomes, is an accurate marker of sex in more than 99% of births.[70] [71] [72]

The sex of the remaining 0.01 to 0.02%—who appear ambiguous due to underdeveloped genitalia or misalignment with chromosomes and phenotype—can be ascertained by analyzing genes, gonadal tissue, and internal genitalia. For example, a 46:XX karyotype almost always indicates female sex, but 1 in 20,000 males have 46:XX, so it is not to be confused with sex itself.[73] Another example is Congenital Adrenal Hyperplasia in 46:XX females, where a gene mutation results in the overproduction of male-making hormones known as androgens.[74] This causes a larger clitoris and partial fusion of the labia.[75] Their sex can be ascertained by looking at structures that play a direct role in the large gamete reproductive strategy: they have ovaries and Fallopian tubes, a uterus, a cervix, and vagina. In other words, they have the phenotype that produces eggs.

Identifying male and female requires understanding the role of primary reproductive anatomy, like gonads and genitalia, in relationship to gamete production and release, something the sex spectrum always ignores. Unlike the claims of the social principle, there are indeed consistent and reliable criteria for distinguishing male and female, linked back to the structures that produce and release either gamete type.

However, if the sex spectrum social principle is accepted, that male and female are social constructs, then the bridge between the biological and political principles is established. Theorists and activists then have the rhetorical upper hand for achieving their final goal of replacing sex with gender identity in most, if not all, spheres of life.

SEX SPECTRUM POLITICAL PRINCIPLE

One's internal sense of whether one is male, female, both, or neither (also known as gender identity) determines sex.

The application of the political principle marks the conclusion of the sex spectrum argument and the goal of theorists and activists: to deconstruct male and female and replace them with subjective identity.

This should not be taken lightly. If one's internal sense of self can replace sex in legal, medical, and social spheres, this can lead to the dissolution of the rights and safety of men and women. Understanding the differences between males and females is critical to our health and rights as individuals and the progress of our societies.

For example, if we abandon sex as an important category in our society, how can we conduct safe and effective medical research and treatment; fight sex-based injustices; record accurate crime statistics; maintain fair, safe, and competitive sports categories; and implement equal opportunities for both sexes?

One can certainly identify freely, but there is a limit to one's speech and actions. Such rights end when one infringes on another's rights, by forcing a person to speak against their own conscience, by infringing on a person's right to fair competition in sports, or by violating one's right to single-sex spaces. Replacing sex with one's internal sense of self in legal, medical, and social spheres is likely to violate all such rights if sex is not recognized as an important category.

If the reality of the two sexes is so profound, why has the sex spectrum argument become so effective? There are two main reasons. One appeals to people's need to feel knowledgeable (the appeal to knowledge), and the other appeals to people's need to feel morally virtuous (the appeal to morals).

The first reason for the effectiveness of the sex spectrum can be found in its appeal to knowledge. The sex spectrum relies on arguments that sound complex, scientific, and even profound, and this makes them easy to believe. People enjoy learning about complexity in biology, especially when it is presented as new and fashionable science that unveils the "true reality." They also feel better about themselves when they believe they align with the latest scientific discoveries. From the activist perspective, those who agree with the sex spectrum's false reality are viewed as educated, knowledgeable, and intelligent, whereas those who disagree are considered uneducated, ignorant, or stupid. Portraying those who agree with the sex spectrum as scientifically minded and those who disagree as scientifically backward is a prime driver of its popular appeal.

The second reason for the effectiveness of the sex spectrum can be found in its appeal to morals. The moral framework claims those who agree with its principles—*that sex is a mix of traits between male and female, that male and female are socially constructed, and that gender identity should replace sex*—are morally virtuous, whereas those who disagree with its principles are morally inferior. To reject such principles even after knowing the science presented, there must be something wrong with you as a person; you must be a hateful, bigoted person who wants to take away people's rights—a transphobe, an intersexphobe, or other buzzwords used as moral hammers against disagreement. This false moral framework captures people's compassion, empathy, and virtue and twists it for political gain. People who are sensitive to the feelings, emotions, and experiences of others, especially to those who are deemed victims or vulnerable minorities of society, are highly susceptible to believing in the sex spectrum's principles.

It should be obvious for those who are truly open-minded that one can disagree with the sex spectrum and its principles while still accepting the diversity of anatomy, physiology, and behavior between all people. For many theorists and activists, however, there is no other option other than agreement with the principles of the sex spectrum if you are to be viewed as both scientifically educated and virtuous.

THE WAY FORWARD

If we wish to show acceptance and compassion to those who are different, stand for important boundaries in society, and further the continuation of scientific knowledge, the sex spectrum is not the answer. The sex spectrum tells us that male and female are undefinable categories and that a person's subjective sense of self is the ultimate determinant of sex. But this is not a scientific nor healthy view.

Sex spectrum proponents ironically forget that differences in reproductive anatomy and sexual behavior within humans only exist because the two sexes exist. Without male and female, there would be no basis for any of these things.

Understanding what the two sexes are and why they exist is not ignoring difference at all. In fact, knowledge of sex differences helps us understand diversity in anatomy, physiology, and behavior within the correct evolutionary and developmental framework. It helps us provide accurate medical treatment to those with developmental disorders like DSDs or psychological conditions like gender dysphoria; it helps us celebrate healthy differences between all people without excluding them from their sex; and finally, knowledge of male and female helps unite the extensive body of research on the evolution and development of the two sexes across the vast diversity of life.

For the rest of the book, we will be analyzing the most popular sex spectrum arguments used across social media, science magazines, and peer-reviewed journals.

CHAPTER REFERENCES

1. Lehtonen, J., Kokko, H., Parker, GA. (2016). What do isogamous organisms teach us about sex and the two sexes? *PTBS, 371(1706),* 1-12.
2. Hörandl, E., Hadacek, F. (2020). Oxygen, life forms, and the evolution of sexes in multicellular eukaryotes. *Heredity, 125(1-14).*
3. Otto, S. (2009). The evolutionary enigma of sex. *The American Naturalist, 174(S1),* 1-14.
4. Muyle, A., Marais, G. (2016). Mating systems in plants and genome evolution. *Encyclopedia of Evolutionary Biology, Academic Press,* 480-492.
5. Holub, A., Shackelford, T. (2021). Gonochorism. *Encyclopedia of Animal Cognition and Behavior. Springer.*
6. Otto, S. (2008). Sexual reproduction and the evolution of sex. *Nature Education, 1(1).*
7. Lehtonen, J., Parker, G. (2014). Gamete competition, gamete limitation, and the evolution of two sexes. *Molecular Human Reproduction, 20(12).*
8. Kumar et al. (2019). Anisogamy. *Encyclopedia of Animal Cognition and Behavior.*
9. Lehtonen, J. (2017). Gamete size. *Encyclopedia of Evolutionary Psychological Science.*
10. Kirk, D. (2006). Oogamy: Inventing the sexes. *Current Biology, 16(24).*
11. Lehtonen, J., Parker, G. (2014). Gamete competition, gamete limitation, and the evolution of two sexes. *Molecular Human Reproduction, 20(12).*
12. Avise, J. (2011). *Hermaphroditism: A primer on the biology, ecology, and the evolution of dual sexuality.* Columbia University Press.
13. Holub, A., Shackelford, T. (2021). Gonochorism. *Encyclopedia of Animal Cognition and Behavior. Springer.*
14. Schärer, L. (2017). The varied ways of being male and female. *Molecular Reproduction & Development, 84.*

15. Rubin, G. (1984). Thinking sex: notes for a radical theory of the politics of sexuality. In: *Pleasure and Danger: Exploring Female Sexuality.* Duke University Press.
16. Butler, J. (1999). *Gender trouble.* Routledge.
17. Fausto-Sterling, A. (2000). *Sexing the body: Gender politics and the construction of sexuality.* Basic Books.
18. Ryle, R. (2015). *Questioning gender: A sociological exploration, 4th ed.* Sage Publications.
19. Ainsworth, C. (2015). Sex redefined: The idea of two sexes is overly simplistic. *Nature, 518,* 288-291.
20. McDonough, M. (2022). How medicine's fixation on the sex binary harms intersex people. From: "A Question of Sex, Episode 2." *Scientific American.*
21. Ryle, R. (2015).
22. (2019). Legal enforcement guidance on discrimination on the basis of gender identity or expression. *NYC Commission on Human Rights.*
23. Jones, T., et al. (2016). *Intersex, Stories and Statistics from Australia.* OpenBook Publishers. 33.
24. Del Guidice, M. (2021). Ideological bias in the Psychology of Sex and Gender. In: *Political Bias in Psychology: Nature, scope, and solutions.* Springer.
25. Lehtonen, J. (2021). The legacy of Parker, Baker, and Smith 1972: Gamete competition, the evolution of anisogamy, and model robustness. *Cells, 10(573).*
26. Rey, R., Josso, N., Racine, C. (2020). Sexual differentiation. In: *Endotext.* South Dartmouth, MDText, Inc.
27. Wilhelm, D., Palmer, S., Koopman, P. (2007). Sex determination and gonadal development in mammals. *Physiological Reviews, 87,* 1-28.
28. Del Guidice, M. (2019). Measuring sex differences and similarities. In: *Gender and sexuality development: Contemporary theory and research.* Springer.
29. Del Guidice, M. (2021).
30. Kennon, J. (2013). The 6 Most Common Biological Sexes in Humans. *Joshuakennon.com.*
31. NIH. (2020). Turner syndrome. *National Library of Medicine.*

32. NIH. (2020). Klinefelter syndrome. *National Library of Medicine.*
33. Warr, N., et al. (2012). The molecular and cellular basis of gonadal sex reversal in mice and humans. *WIREs Dev Bio, 1.*
34. Nagahama, Y., et al. (2021). Sex determination, gonadal sex differentiation, and plasticity in vertebrate species. *Physiological Reviews, 101(3),* 1237-1308.
35. Witchel, S. (2018). Disorders of sex development. *Best Practice and Research in Clinical Obstetrics and Gynecology, 48.*
36. Eggers, S., Sinclair, A. (2012). Mammalian sex determination: Insights from humans and mice. *Chromosome Res, 20.*
37. NIH. (2019). Classic congenital adrenal hyperplasia due to 21-hydroxylase deficiency. *Genetic and Rare Diseases Information Center.*
38. Bachtrog, D., Mank, J.E., Peichel, C.L., Kirkpatrick, M., Otto, S.P., Ashman, T.L., et al. (2014). Sex determination: Why so many ways of doing it? *PLoS Biol, 12(7).*
39. Beukeboom, L, Perrin, N. (2014). *The evolution of sex determination.* Oxford, UK: Oxford University Press.
40. González, E., Martínez-López, M., Morales-Garduza, M. et al. (2019). The sex-determination pattern in crocodilians: A systematic review of three decades of research. *J Anim Ecol, 88,* 1417-1427.
41. Hilton, E. (2021). Crocodiles use temperature-dependent mechanisms of sex. *Twitter.*
42. Lipinska et al. (2015). Sexual dimorphism and the evolution of sex-biased gene expression in the brown alga Ectocarpus. *Molecular Biology and Evolution, 32(6),* 1583.
43. Parker, G.A. (2014). The sexual cascade and the rise of pre-ejaculatory sexual selection, sex roles, and sexual conflict. *CSH Persp Bio.*
44. Lehtonen, J., Parker, G. (2014). Gamete competition, gamete limitation, and the evolution of two sexes. *Molecular Human Reproduction, 20(12).*
45. Cooke, L. (2019). Everything you know about hyenas is wrong—these animals are fierce, social, and incredibly smart. *Ted Ideas.*

46. Cunha, G., et al. (2005). The ontogeny of the urogenital system of the spotted hyena. *Biology of Reproduction, 73,* 554-564.
47. Thresher, R. (1984). *Reproduction in reef fishes.* T.F.H. Publications, Inc., New Jersey.
48. Fautin & Allen. (1992). *Anemone fishes and their host sea anemones, a guide for aquarists and divers.* Western Australian Museum, Perth, p. 160.
49. Khoo, LM., et al. (2018). Growth pattern, diet, and reproductive biology of the clownfish Amphiprion ocellaris in waters of Pulau Tioman, Malaysia. *The Egyptian Journal of Aquatic Research, 44(3),* 233-239.
50. Stolting, K. N., Wilson, A.B. (2007). Male pregnancy in seahorses and pipefish: beyond the mammalian model. *Bioessays, 29,* 884-896.
51. Schärer, L., Janicke, T., Ramm, A. (2015). Sexual conflict in hermaphrodites. *Cold Spring Harb Perspect Biol, 7.*
52. Atwood, M. (2020). Slug sex as an exception to male and female. *Twitter.*
53. Charlesworth, D. (2002). Plant sex determination and sex chromosomes. *Heredity, 88,* 94-101.
54. Holub, A., Shackelford, T. (2021). Gonochorism. *Encyclopedia of Animal Cognition and Behavior. Springer.*
55. Warr, N., et al. (2012). The molecular and cellular basis of gonadal sex reversal in mice and humans. *WIREs Dev Bio, 1.*
56. Bashamboo, A., et al. (2017). Anomalies in human sex determination provide unique insights into the complex genetic; interactions of early gonad development. *Clinical Genetics, 91,* 143-156.
57. Witchel, S. (2018). Disorders of sex development. *Best Practice and Research in Clinical Obstetrics and Gynecology, 48.*
58. Jones, R., Lopez, K. (2014). Sexual differentiation. In: *Human Reproductive Biology, 4th edition.* Elsevier.
59. Rosenfield, K. (2018). Hermaphrodite. *Encyclopedia of Animal Cognition and Behavior.*
60. Lehtonen, J., Kokko, H., Parker, GA. (2016). What do isogamous organisms teach us about sex and the two sexes? *PTBS, 371(1706),* 1-12.

61. Lehtonen, J., Parker, G. (2014). Gamete competition, gamete limitation, and the evolution of two sexes. *Molecular Human Reproduction, 20(12).*
62. Perrin, N. (2011). What uses are mating types? The developmental switch model. *Evolution, 66(4),* 947-956.
63. Lehtonen, J., Parker, G. (2014).
64. Lessov-Schlaggar, C., et al. (2016). The fallacy of univariate solutions to complex systems problems. *Frontiers in Neuroscience, 10(267).*
65. Bruce, V., et al. (1993). Sex discrimination: How do we tell the difference between male and female faces? *Perception, 22,* 131-152.
66. Chekroud, A., et al. (2016). Patterns in the human brain mosaic discriminate males from females. *PNAS Letter to Joel et al.*
67. Del Guidice M., Lippa R., Puts D., Bailey D., Bailey M., Schmitt D. (2016). Joel et al's method systematically fails to detect large, consistent sex differences. *PNAS, 113(14).*
68. Del Guidice, M. (2009). On the real magnitude of psychological sex differences. *Evolutionary Psychology, 7(2),* 264-279.
69. Sax, L. (2002). How common is intersex? A response to Anne Fausto-Sterling. *The Journal of Sex Research, 39(3).*
70. Maeda et al (1991). A cytogenetic survey of 14,835 consecutive liveborns. *The Japanese Journal of Genetics, 36(1),* 117-129.
71. Hamerton et al (1975). A cytogenetic survey of 14,069 newborn infants. I. Incidence of chromosome abnormalities. *Clinical Genetics, 8(4),* 223-243
72. Nielsen & Sillesen (1975). Incidence of chromosome aberrations among 11,148 newborn children. *Human Genetics, 30(1),* 1-12.
73. de la Chapelle, A. (1981). The etiology of maleness in XX men. *Human Genetics, 58,* 105-116.
74. Kovacs, J., et al. (2001). Lessons from 30 years of clinical diagnosis and treatment of CAH. *J Clin Endocrinol Metab, 86(7),* 2958-64.
75. NIH. (2019). Classic congenital adrenal hyperplasia due to 21-hydroxylase deficiency. *Genetic and Rare Diseases Information Center.*

ARGUMENT 1

"THE SIX MOST COMMON BIOLOGICAL SEXES IN HUMANS"

JOSHUAKENNON.COM

One common technique the sex spectrum uses is to conflate sex determination mechanisms, genetic and environmental factors that drive sex development, with sex.[1] No other article represents this better than Joshua Kennon's "The Six Most Common Biological Sexes in Humans."

The main argument of Kennon's piece is that there are six common biological sexes in humans, resulting in millions of people who are not male or female. He writes:

> We know, without question, that humans are not just born male and female. There are at least six biological sexes that can result in fairly normal lifespans.

Sexes are the phenotypes that produce sperm or eggs; humans have only two.[2] So, what are these six biological sexes? Kennon answers this question by listing the two typical karyotypes (chromosome combinations) in humans (XX and XY) along with four chromosomal disorders:

> The six biological karyotype sexes that do not result in death to the fetus are:
>
> - X – Roughly 1 in 2,000 to 1 in 5,000 (Turner's)
> - XX – Most common form of female

- XXY – Roughly 1 in 500 to 1 in 1,000 (Klinefelter)
- XY – Most common form of male
- XYY – Roughly 1 out of 1,000 people
- XXXY – Roughly 1 in 18,000 to 1 in 50,000 births."

This is the trick: in one moment, Kennon is talking about six sexes, and the next moment he is talking about six karyotypes. Those who are not attentive to the switch assume along with Kennon that karyotypes are sexes and that any atypical variation in karyotype is a separate and distinct sex. Thus, many miss the sleight-of-hand trick: *the conflation of chromosomes with sex.*

The sex chromosomes X and Y, along with the autosomes (non sex chromosomes), hold genetic instructions which encode the development of one's sex; they hold the genetic sex determination mechanisms, but they are not the same thing as sex. Humans usually have 22 pairs of autosomes and a 23rd pair of chromosomes known as the sex chromosomes (XX or XY), making 46:XX or 46:XY.

The four atypical karyotypes of X, XXY, XYY, and XXXY all occur from genetic errors during cell division in the parent's gametes, known as nondisjunction, where chromosomes are not distributed equally among sperm or egg cells. During typical reproductive cell division, each egg gets a single X chromosome, and each sperm gets either an X chromosome or a Y. This results in a fetus with either XX or XY.

However, with nondisjunction, an egg or sperm may end up with an atypical distribution of chromosomes, resulting in conditions like Klinefelter syndrome (XXY). If an egg with an extra X chromosome (XX) is fertilized by a sperm cell with a Y chromosome (Y), the fetus will have Klinefelter syndrome. And if a sperm with both an X and a Y chromosome (XY) fertilizes an egg with an X chromosome (X), the fetus will also have Klinefelter syndrome.[3] The same concept applies to karyotypes of X, XYY, and XXXY, all of which result from nondisjunction. These chromosomal disorders often result in infertility and life-threating complications.

So, why do these chromosomal disorders not form additional sexes, as Kennon claims? This is because genetic sex determination in mammals is binary, meaning the genetic systems result in just two sexes, even for those with chromosomal disorders.[4]

Barring more obscure genetic mutations that we will explore later, humans who have a Y chromosome with male-making genes like the sex-determining gene, SRY, develop testes and a penis, the small gamete phenotype (male). And those with no Y (no SRY) and female-making genes develop ovaries, Fallopian tubes, a uterus, and a vagina, the large gamete phenotype (female). For example, fetuses with a karyotype of 45:X do not have a Y chromosome with the SRY gene, so they develop as females,[5] whereas fetuses with a karyotype of 47:XXY do have a Y chromosome with the SRY gene, so they develop as males.[6] No matter how many X chromosomes or Y chromosomes you add, the end result remains the same: males or females.

Knowing this concept, that sex determination in humans largely occurs through the activation of the SRY gene on the Y chromosome, we can rewrite Kennon's list of karyotypes and predict the resulting sex:

- X – Female
- XX – Female
- XXY – Male
- XY – Male
- XYY – Male
- XXXY – Male

Assuming that chromosomes are sex can result in strange conclusions, such as thinking that a person with two Y chromosomes (XYY) must be more male than someone with only one Y chromosome (XY). But the truth is extra X chromosomes do not make you more female and extra Y chromosomes do not make you more male. In fact, the sex chromosomes X and Y do not hold the essence of femaleness and maleness for two reasons: First, most genes essential for sex development are located on the autosomes, not the sex chromosomes.[7] Second, and most importantly, sexes are not chromosomes. We could switch around the information on the chromosomes, such as translocating the SRY gene onto an X, and get different outcomes—such as a male with XX or a female with XY.[8]

Sexes are the phenotypes that produce sperm or ova, and chromosomes simply hold the genetic instructions which lead to sex development. Atypical chromosome combinations do not result in new sexes; they result in males or females with congenital medical conditions.

By conflating sex with chromosome variation, Joshua Kennon ignores the biological definition of sex, and claims there are more than two sexes in humans. This only works on those who do not know the difference between chromosomes and sex.

Another strange and curious conclusion occurs if we take the logic of sex determination mechanisms = sex and apply it to other species. For our example, the sex of crocodiles is determined not by chromosomes but by environmental temperature. This means that a range of temperatures determine which eggs develop as males and which develop as females. Temperatures around 33 C and above result in males, and temperatures around 30 C result in females.[9] If we apply the logic of *sex determination mechanisms = sex* to crocodiles just as Kennon applies it to humans, then each temp value in crocodiles would be a sex. In fact, they would have infinite sexes, named 30.1 C, 30.2 C, 30.3 C, and so on.

Of course, we know why this is absurd. Temperature values are not sex; rather, they regulate crocodilian sex development, resulting in crocodiles with the small gamete phenotype (male) or crocodiles with the large gamete phenotype (female). Atypical temperature values do not form new sexes in crocodiles just as atypical karyotypes do not form new sexes in humans. Temp values are to sex in crocodiles as genes are to sex in humans: they are the systems that trigger the development of one's sex. Confusing sex determination mechanisms for sex is like confusing the ingredients of a cake for the cake itself.

Theorists and activists who claim that karyotype variation forms new sexes are using a common strategies from the sex spectrum's biological principle: conflate sex determination mechanisms with sex. One moment, they will be discussing karyotype, and the next, sex, without defining the difference. And yet none of these karyotypes result in a third sex; instead, they result in precisely two: males or females. Thus, they are not additional sexes.

SUMMARY

- Karyotypes are chromosome combinations, not sexes.
- Chromosomes hold the genes that develop one's sex.
- Sex is defined by gamete type and observed by the reproductive anatomy that produces and releases either gamete.
- No matter the number of Xs or Ys, the result is male or female.

CHAPTER REFERENCES

1. Eggers, S., Sinclair, A. (2012). Mammalian sex determination: Insights from humans and mice. *Chromosome Res, 20.*
2. Lehtonen, J., Parker, G. (2014). Gamete competition, gamete limitation, and the evolution of two sexes. *Molecular Human Reproduction, 20(12).*
3. NIH. (2020). Klinefelter Syndrome. *MedlinePlus Genetics.*
4. Kimball, J. (2020). Sex chromosomes. *LibreText.org.*
5. NIH. (2020). Turner Syndrome. *MedlinePlus Genetics.*
6. NIH. (2020). Klinefelter Syndrome. *MedlinePlus Genetics.*
7. Leon, N., Reyes, A., Harley, V. (2019). Differences of sex development: the road to diagnosis. *Lancet Diabetes Endocrinology, 7(7),* 2.
8. Weber, C. & Capel, B. (2018). Sex reversal. *Current Biology, 28(21),* R1234-R1236.
9. González, E., Martínez-López, M., Morales-Garduza, M., et al. (2019). The sex-determination pattern in crocodilians: A systematic review of three decades of research. *J Anim Ecol, 88.*

ARGUMENT 2

"SCIENCEVET'S SPECTRUM"

TWITTER

If you really wanted people to believe in something that was false, you might paint it as a cutting-edge scientific discovery, something that has replaced the "old science" of days long gone. Appealing to people's hunger for knowledge, especially knowledge that seems to challenge existing assumptions, can be a powerful solvent.

While the masses are generally perceived as too close-minded and detached from cutting-edge discoveries and forward progress, it is likely the inverse in our postmodern era: people may be too open-minded and receptive. It can be argued the masses are so open-minded their hyper-receptiveness to novel ideas has decayed their critical thinking skills. This is immensely true in the age of the internet, where false information spreads like wildfire, and the hyper-receptive masses are the dead wood.

Open-mindedness and receptivity are virtues and vices; virtues under the right circumstances, and vices when overindulged. You can in fact be too open-minded to the point your brains fall out, or too receptive to the point you let others take advantage of you.

This is why one sex spectrum Twitter thread by an account named ScienceVet became so popular, not because there was new science presented, but because the existing science around sex development was painted in a way that seemed to challenge people's existing assumptions and cater to their compassion. However, the view of sex presented by ScienceVet is pseudoscience, not cutting-edge science. Most who agreed with the thread did so under the pretense they were learning about new and exciting knowledge; they were just not critical enough to examine its false assumptions.

ScienceVet's thread was retweeted over 23,000 times and counting, boosting his followers to over 10,000 almost overnight. Let's analyze his argument with peer-reviewed science.

DEFINING SEX

ScienceVet's employs the sex spectrum's first two principles: the biological (sex is a continuum between male and female) and the social (there is no single criteria for differentiating between male and female). He begins with the biological principle by claiming that sex is defined by variation of anatomy and physiology:

> Hi new people! We're gonna talk about sex. Like physical sex! Because there's some confusion. First, sex defined: We're talking physical sex here, not gender. Body parts, hormones, and genetics (and more). Biological sex is a spectrum.

As in most sex spectrum arguments, there will be no mention of reproduction here. After detaching sex from its role in reproduction, and reducing it to a mix of independent body parts, ScienceVet argues that variation in anatomy and physiology is equal to a spectrum of sex. Next, he sets up a strawman: that we, including scientists, all thought XX was the definition of female and XY the definition of male:

> Everyone's super familiar with the XX/XY dichotomy, right? What we all learned in like 4th grade? And that's great, it gives you a starting point. But it's only the very starting point. The idea is, XX is girl, XY is boy, right?

Portraying the XX-XY dichotomy as the old definition of female and male does two things: first, it makes people feel like they need to update their way of thinking. You wouldn't want to be stuck in 4th grade biology, now would you? And second, it creates the false premise that biologists thought the sexes were defined by chromosome combinations, rather than their role in reproduction. Of course, biologists never thought the sexes were chromosomes. They knew what the sexes were well before we found the mechanisms that regulate sex development.

APPROPRIATING ATYPICAL DEVELOPMENT

By defining sex as a mix of traits detached from reproduction, ScienceVet then has the unstable foundation for using people with developmental conditions as exceptions to male and female. Once people believe that male and female are only defined through a cluster of traits, like XY = male and XX = female, then they are likely to believe a person with an atypical cluster is not male or female. This is where ScienceVet goes next:

> The idea is, XX is girl, XY is boy, right? Welllll... that's not totally right. There are XY people, who have ovaries! And give birth! AH! And XX people who have male bodies and functional sperm! Double AH!

ScienceVet is correct those who have XY can sometimes develop as females, and those with XX can sometimes develop as males, but this is no exception to sex being binary. In fact, these cases underline just how robust the binary is by showing that atypical development still results in male and female sexes.

Let's take a quick look at these two atypical cases. First, ScienceVet uses the example of the 46:XY woman who gave birth. She was able to give birth because she had a mosaic karyotype. Likely through a cell division error during embryonic development, some of her cells were 46:XY and others divided into 45:X and 46:XX. She was a typical female with ovaries, Fallopian tubes, a uterus, cervix, and vagina.[1] Because she developed the phenotype that produces large gametes, she is female. Another example is a 46:XY girl, no mosaicism, with normal ovaries and a healthy female reproductive system. Geneticists found she was missing CBX2, a critical gene upstream of SRY. Without it, SRY cannot do its job, and the fetus developed as a female.[2]

What about the cases of XX males? Fetuses with XX can sometimes develop as males thanks to a translocation of the SRY gene onto an X chromosome during cell division in the father's sperm cells.[3] A translocation of the SRY gene is the cause for 80-90% of XX male cases.[4] If a sperm with an X chromosome and the SRY gene fuses with an egg that has one X chromosome, the result will usually be an XX male.

The SRY gene initiates a complex set of gene cascades leading to male development: the bipotential gonads differentiate into testes. The testes release testosterone which build the sperm transportation systems, and they also release anti-Müllerian hormone, which disintegrates the structures that would have become the internal female genitalia. Testosterone is then converted into dihydrotestosterone, which causes the testes to descend and the external male genitalia to form. Thus, XX males develop the phenotype that produces sperm, and so they are males.

However, because XX males do not have the AZF region, a genetic region found on the Y chromosome that causes young sperm cells to develop into mature sperm, they are unable to produce viable sperm in their ejaculate. Opposite of what ScienceVet claims, there has been no documented case of an XX male in humans producing viable sperm.[5] But such males do have the phenotypic structures necessary to do so. The biological definition of the sexes shows us that the two cases ScienceVet describes (XX males and XY females) do not exist outside the binary but, rather, are examples of genetic disorders within the binary.

ScienceVet then continues applying the second strategy of the sex spectrum by listing more variations. He writes:

> [There's] (XXY, XYY, Y, X, XX with translocation, XY with deletion) to hormonal (Androgen Insensitivity, Estradiol failure).

This is true, but all these cases are still male or female. 47:XXY individuals develop as males thanks to the activation of the SRY gene and successful androgen reception.[6] 45:Y fetuses do not survive since one X chromosome is required for development.[7] 46:XX with SRY translocation is the XX male case described above, and 46:XY with SRY deletion results in female development.[8]

Thus, rather than proving sex itself is on a spectrum, all these cases show us the amazing stability of the two evolved reproductive roles of male and female. Even with chromosomal or hormonal anomalies, the fetus still develops as a male or female.

THE BIMODAL ARGUMENT

After presenting cases of atypical development as supposed exceptions to the male-female binary, ScienceVet claims all these diverse characteristics form a bimodal distribution. This means, in his eyes, that sex is not binary but bimodal. The claim by ScienceVet is that the two averages in the distribution (the peaks) represent clusters of traits we associate with male and female, and that any deviation from these two averages (such as the middle portion) represents people who are not male or female. There are many fundamental problems to consider when sex spectrum proponents like ScienceVet claim that sex is a bimodal distribution.

What does the X-axis of this bimodal distribution represent? If it is 'sex,' how do you quantify it? What are the units of 'sex'? If this distribution represents many characteristics aggregated together, shouldn't each characteristic get its own distribution?

For instance, it does not make much sense to aggregate testosterone levels with genital morphology into one distribution and one unit. They are separate traits that are quantitatively and qualitatively differently (different in number and form). So, shouldn't we be analyzing each trait separately, with a separate distribution? How do we predict who is more male and who is more female on this "distribution of sex"? What specific characteristics tell us the answer? If I am an XX male, where am I placed on the graph? If I am a typical female but have three X chromosomes, where am I placed? If we are using genitalia, hormone levels, or even chromosomes, why are those characteristics chosen? How are they ordered on the X-axis and why? Is it arbitrary? If it is, why are we using this?

First, when we find that data is arranged in a bimodal distribution, this usually indicates we have two different groups within the data.[9] The same applies to differences between males and females, where singular traits like testosterone levels and height arrange themselves into a bimodal distribution. Inside this bimodal distribution represents one group (males) and another group (females). Disaggregating the data (separating the two distributions) allows us to analyze the distribution for males and females separately.

For many sex differences, bimodal distributions comprise one distribution of a given trait for males and one distribution of that same trait for females plotted onto the same graph. Overlap between the two distributions does not represent people who are "between" male and female; rather, it represents the values of a trait where males and females share commonalities. For example, height values between males and females overlap significantly,[10] and personality differences overlap even more.[11] In both cases, there are still only two groups being compared: males and females. Thus, the only reason why sex differences form bimodal distributions in the first place is because there are only two sexes. There are only two groups being compared.

What's more, it does not follow logically how one would plot 'sex' on a bimodal distribution. There is no way to quantify sex as a unit because it is a category of living things, divided into male and female based on the binary variable of reproduction. The characteristics related to sex—chromosomes, gonads, hormones, and genitals—are not independent traits but clusters of dependent characteristics that support the male and female functions. They make up the reproductive *system*. But ScienceVet and other proponents of the sex spectrum wish to detach sex characteristics from the system they are a part of so they can argue that sex exists on a spectrum and that male and female are unreliable categories.

Developmental biologist Emma Hilton explores this phenomenon of sex spectrum proponents wanting to detach sex characteristics from their evolutionary and developmental systems:

> Some people are utterly incurious about how bodies work, about how systems are formed, about 'why' a distribution looks like that. The dissociation of sex characteristics as individual markers that can be reduced to cataloguing is frustrating to watch from an academic point-of-view.
>
> These characteristics are not independent of each other. They are individually part of a system, and, in most people, they correlate completely. They are not a random assortment of stuff that happens, for the most part, to coincide as if by magic.
>
> 'Some people have got penises,'... 'Some people have got testes,'... 'Some people have got hairy chests,' Yes. And they tend to be the same people. Weird, huh? Anyone with a remotely questioning mind, and most definitely anyone claiming scientific credentials, should immediately be asking, 'Why does that happen? Why do people tend to have penises, testes, and hairy chests—or—ovaries, vulvas and breast tissues?'
>
> I often ask for characteristics for a given Sex Score. 'I am the red dot, describe something about my sex characteristics.' Someone once said that a red dot in the mirrored position to that below meant I probably had soft skin and was a bit of a tomboy. No comprehension that two people with the same Sex Score could have very different sets of sex characteristics.

> And their attempts to quantify discrete categories by assigning scores to, say, chromosome conformation always reveal bias from their previous-existing knowledge (that XX is typically female and XY is typically male). Because when constructing an order of sex chromosomes, they almost always anchor to XX and XY. Because they know.[12]

ScienceVet is not describing sex as biologists understand it—evolved systems—but as a mix of traits that can all be independent from one another. This makes his sex spectrum bimodal graph rather useless because it lacks all descriptive, predictive, and explanatory power. It therefore has zero scientific validity. There is no way to know who sits where on the graph and why, since all these distinct traits (chromosomes, genes, gonads, genitalia, hormones) have been blended into one spectral smoothie, making it nothing more than just a pretty picture and a useful rhetorical device for theorists and activists.

Detaching sex characteristics from the role they play in reproduction is a superficial view of biological systems, because it is purely descriptive, lacking any explanatory and predictive power. It would be like reducing eyes to the descriptions of their different cells while not explaining how these cells work together in a functioning system, or like saying that kidneys are just a mix of different characteristics that exist on a spectrum, without understanding how these different traits work in concert to produce an overarching function.

INDIVIDUAL VARIATION

After detaching male and female from their different roles in reproduction and conflating variation of bodily traits with additional sexes, ScienceVet now employs the sex spectrum's social principle to argue that there are not two kinds of distinguishable male and female bodies in the world. He claims the more we explore the diversity of traits between people, the more we can break down people's 'sex' into smaller and smaller differences—so much so that we can place each person's sex into its own unique bin, rather than just 'male' or 'female.' He writes:

> We can keep breaking down your biological sex into smaller and smaller differences in brain areas, hormone levels, signaling differences, genetic variances. There is nothing stopping us from binning every individual into their own bin.

This might make sense if one needs to analyze someone's specific mix of traits for medical purposes. For example, each person has a unique height and weight mixed with different hormone levels. It would be important to understand these subtleties without assuming that someone who is male will always be 6'-0" and 200 pounds, with high levels of testosterone, while someone who is female will always be 5'-2" and 120 pounds, and with low levels of testosterone.

At the same time, it is imperative we know what a healthy male and female system looks like if we are to accurately treat diseases and disorders. For example, men's and women's testosterone levels almost never overlap. The highest female range is usually 5 times lower than the lowest male levels. Males tend to have 15-20 times more testosterone than the average female.[13] Thus, female-level testosterone in a male or male-level T in a female might indicate a hormonal disorder. But we can only treat such a disorder if we know what male and female are in the first place. ScienceVet's strategy of binning every individual into their own bin is reductive, in that it looks at trait differences separately without trying to understand them within an evolved system. This can be useful in specific contexts, but it is not useful in all circumstances nor even most circumstances. Anatomy and physiology are highly contingent on the interactions of many constituent elements working together within an entire system. Understanding how bodily systems function as interconnected networks is just as critical to effective medical treatment as analyzing singular traits. Yet ScienceVet doubles down:

> The thing to remember is that this is not "new." We are not 'inventing sexes' here. Sex has ALWAYS been this curve. We were just using REALLY BIG bins. And now we're realizing that that's not representative of biology, it's inhibiting understanding of medicine and biology.

Our understanding of male and female as two different systems only inhibits our understanding of medicine and biology if we have a narrow view of what male and female are supposed to look like. Exploring how male and female reproductive systems work in concert with a host of different sex characteristics and physiology gives us a much greater and more comprehensive understanding compared to if we analyzed each trait separately. Reducing people to singular traits, without realizing how those traits play a role in a functional system, would be rather damaging to effective medical treatment, because it fails to understand how singular traits (like gonads) are contingent on other traits (like hormone levels).

We can indeed explore the objective reality of male and female without becoming too narrow in our views of bodily variation. There are many males who have much lower testosterone than the average male, and there are females who have much higher testosterone than the average female; there are females who are taller than some males, and males who are shorter than some females; and there are some males who develop with XX chromosomes, and some females who develop with XY chromosomes. When we understand the sexes as functional systems and bodily diversity as the expected variation within those systems, we can cultivate a more nuanced view of sex.

ScienceVet seems to think that if we get rid of the categories of male and female and reduce people's traits to singular entities detached from system function, then we can achieve better medicine, but this gets it exactly wrong. Rather than expanding the definition of male and female, we need to better understand the processes which form the variation within males and variation within females.[14] As developmental biologist Emma Hilton writes, "It's not that the 'male' and 'female' boxes have to get bigger; it's that our understanding of the mechanisms that make males and females has to absorb new data."[15]

In the end, ScienceVet's attempt to deconstruct male and female by detaching sex from reproduction and using medical conditions as supposed exceptions falls flat. The reproductive functions of male and female—producing many small motile gametes (sperm) and producing few large sessile gametes (eggs)—have existed for over a billion years and will continue to exist regardless of our attempts to deny them. Within this system, there is variation of anatomy and physiology, with average traits for males and average traits for females. Thus, it is the variety of traits within males and within females that is bimodal, not male and female themselves.

The truth is that sex is binary, and we do not have to deny this fact to accept and understand the wide diversity of body types, psychology, and expression found within it.

SUMMARY

- ScienceVet's thread conflates sex characteristics with sex.
- Sexes are reproductive roles: the male sex is the phenotype that produces sperm, and the female sex is the phenotype that produces eggs.
- Sex characteristics are the traits that develop to support one's sex. There is variation of traits within males and variation of traits within females. This does not form new sexes nor a spectrum of sex.
- Quantifiable traits within males and females (like hormones) often form one distribution for males and one for females.
- Sex cannot be plotted as a bimodal distribution, since it is a division of living things by organization of the body around either gamete type.

CHAPTER REFERENCES

1. Dumic, M., et al. (2008). Report of fertility in a woman with a predominantly 46,XY karyotype in a family with multiple disorders of sexual development. *The Journal of Clinical Endocrinology and Metabolism, 93(1),* 182-189.
2. Biason-Lauber, A., et al. (2009). Ovaries and female phenotype in a girl with 46,XY karyotype and mutations in the CBX2 gene. *American Journal of Human Genetics, 84,* 658-663.
3. Witchel, S. (2018). Disorders of sex development. *Best Practice and Research in Clinical Obstetrics and Gynecology, 48,* 6.
4. de la Chapelle, A., Hastbacka, J., Korhonen, T., Maenpaa, J. (1990). The etiology of XX sex reversal. *Reproduction, Nutrition, Development, Suppl 1,* 39s–49s.
5. Osaka, A., et al. (2020). SRY-positive 46,XX testicular disorder of sexual development with ledyig cell tumor. *American Journal of Men's Health, 14(5),* 2.
6. Kimball, J. (2020). Sex chromosomes. *LibreText.org.*
7. Schmidt, M. (2018). A second X chromosome could explain why women live longer than men. *Discover Magazine.*
8. NIH. (2020). Swyer syndrome. *MedlinePlus Genetics.*
9. Glen, S. (2013). Bimodal distribution: What is it? *StatisticsHowTo.com.*
10. Roser, M., et al. (2019). Human height. *Our World in Data.*
11. Weisberg, Y., et al. (2011). Gender differences in personality across the ten aspects of the Big Five. *Frontiers in Psychology, 2(178).*
12. Hilton, E. (2021). Dissociation of sex characteristics as individual markers. *Twitter.*
13. Handelsman, D., Hirschberg, A., Bermon, S. (2018). Circulating testosterone as the hormonal basis of sex differences in athletic performance. *Endocrine Reviews, 39(5),* 803-829.
14. McGregor, A., et al. (2017). Sex as a biological variable in emergency medicine research and clinical practice. *Western Journal of Emergency Medicine, 18(6).*
15. Hilton, E. (2018). Response to ScienceVet's 'Sex Spectrum' thread. *Twitter.*

ARGUMENT 3

"LET'S TALK ABOUT SEX"

TWITTER

In 2019, marine biologist Rebecca Helm wrote a Twitter thread about how sex exists on a spectrum. Helm is concerned that the concept of "biological sex" is being weaponized to discriminate against those who identify as trans and non-binary. Because of this, the underlying premise of her thread, like most sex spectrum arguments, is not biological, but rather social and political: male and female are unreliable categories, and others should be able to identify as they see fit on a social and legal level.

The veneer of sound biology helps reinforce the underlying social and political argument, and it is hard to argue it was not a success. Her piece has now become the most shared Twitter thread on the sex spectrum, with almost 60,000 likes and 34,000 retweets as of this writing. For Helm, the key to increasing acceptance of those who are different means male and female must be deconstructed. She writes:

> Friendly neighborhood biologist here. I see a lot of people are talking about biological sexes and gender right now. Lots of folks make biological sex seem really simple. Well, since it's so simple, let's find the biological roots, shall we? Let's talk about sex…

Helm sets up the idea that sex might not be as simple as people make it out to be, arguing that, if it is so simple, "Let's find the biological roots." As she conflates the complexities of sex development with sex, she makes the erroneous point that there is no defining feature differentiating male and female. To understand how she does this, let's explore how her argument functions and what she uses as evidence for the sex spectrum's principles.

The first step in Helm's argument, like most other sex spectrum writings, is to fail to mention what sexes are and instead focus on the various mechanisms (like the SRY gene) and traits (like testosterone levels) involved in their development. Ignoring what sexes fundamentally are is rather odd coming from a marine biologist, but it is this redefinition of sex as a mix of traits detached from reproductive role (sex spectrum biological principle) combined with Helm's credentials (appeal to knowledge) that gives her argument rhetorical power.

Applying this strategy, she begins her thread by exploring atypical combinations of chromosomes, hormones, and cells, claiming there is no single trait we can call "biological sex."

CHROMOSOMES

Helm starts with chromosomes and genetics, writing:

> If you know a bit about biology you will probably say that biological sex is caused by chromosomes, XX and you're female, XY and you're male. This is "chromosomal sex" but is it "biological sex"?
>
> Turns out there is only ONE GENE on the Y chromosome that really matters to sex. It's called the SRY gene. During human embryonic development, the SRY protein turns on male-associated genes. Having an SRY gene makes you "genetically male." But is this "biological sex"?

> Sometimes that SRY gene pops off the Y chromosome and over to an X chromosome. Surprise! So now you've got an X with an SRY and a Y without an SRY. What does this mean? A Y with no SRY means physically you're female, chromosomally you're male (XY) and genetically you're female (no SRY). An X with an SRY means you're physically male, chromosomally female (XX) and genetically male (SRY). But biological sex is simple! There must be another answer...

Helm is using a rhetorical strategy that she continues throughout the entire thread: we thought this trait was the definition of sex, but look at all these exceptions. Thus, there must not be a universal definition of male and female. The supposed "exceptions" she uses to male and female involve people with disorders of sex development who, through genetic mutations or translocations of certain genes, do not develop in the typical way.

However, not developing in the typical way is a much different thing than not developing as a male or female. Helm conflates the two. She claims that a male who develops with a 46:XX karyotype and a female who develops with a 46:XY karyotype are exceptions to male and female, and yet she never once defines the terms male and female. Helm's argument remains rhetorically effective only if male and female are never defined in the context of their different roles in reproduction: the biological definition of sex.

46:XX males and 46:XY females actually fail to be an exception to the categories of male and female once we understand that sexes are not defined by chromosomes but by their reproductive role. 46:XX males are male because they develop the small gamete phenotype (testes and penis),[1] and 46:XY females (like those with Swyer syndrome) are female because they develop the large gamete phenotype (Müllerian structure, vagina, vulva).[2] Thus, after understanding sexes as evolved reproductive mechanisms, it becomes clear that chromosomal disorders for males and females do not render the two categories unreliable;

rather, it shows us how robust the dual system of sex is: that even in the presence of chromosomal or genetic disorders, male and female are still produced.

HORMONES

After using chromosomal and genetic variation to deconstruct the meaning of male and female, Helm moves to hormones. "Is this the root of biological sex?" she asks. She then continues:

> "Hormonal male" means you produce 'normal' levels of male-associated hormones. Except some percentage of females will have higher levels of 'male' hormones than some percentage of males. Ditto ditto 'female' hormones. And if you're developing, your body may not produce enough hormones for your genetic sex, leading you to be genetically male or female, chromosomally male or female, hormonally non-binary, and physically non-binary.

There is a distribution of hormone levels for males and a distribution of hormone levels for females. Just like most other trait variation, atypical levels of hormones do not suddenly mean male and female are unreliable categories: a male with low testosterone and a female with high testosterone remain male and female.

For example, some females are born with a rare condition called Congenital Adrenal Hyperplasia, which results in the over-production of androgens from the adrenal glands. These women are often exposed to male-typical levels of androgens in the womb, sometimes masculinizing the external genitalia, and this can lead to the growth of the clitoris and, if severe enough, fusion of the labia. Despite this, females with CAH are female because they develop the large gamete phenotype.[3] They are also usually fertile, able to produce eggs, gestate, and give birth to offspring. Another example of how atypical hormone levels do not change one's sex or make sex undefinable is 47:XXY Klinefelter syndrome, resulting in males who often have smaller than average testes, low sperm count, lower muscle mass, decreased bone density, and growth of breast tissue.[4] Males with Klinefelter syndrome are male because they develop the small gamete phenotype.[5] They are often infertile, but infertility treatments can sometimes help them produce viable sperm. Both females with CAH and males with 47:XXY are defined as female and male, respectively, not through singular traits, but in the fact their reproductive systems are organized around one or the other gamete.

CELLS

Finally, in her last example, Helm discusses how receptors in cells can sometimes mutate, making them unable to bind to sex hormones. She writes:

> Maybe cells are the answer to "biological sex"?? Right?? Cells have receptors that "hear" the signal from sex hormones. But sometimes those receptors don't work. Like a mobile phone that's on 'do not disturb.' Call and cell, they will not answer.

Depending on the system affected, mutations in receptors can change one's entire anatomy and physiology from what is expected. For example, in a fetus with 46:XY and a mutation in the androgen receptor gene on the X chromosome, sex hormones produced from the developing testes fail to bind to androgen receptors, leaving excess testosterone with nowhere to go. Unable to find a home, large amounts of testosterone are then converted into estrogen through a process called aromatase.[6] This results in the baby developing the rest of the way down the female path instead, with a vulva and vagina, Müllerian ducts that fail to develop, and Wolffian ducts that never fully develop either.

The resulting condition type is known as a *sex reversal*, where the fetus began developing down one reproductive pathway (in this case, the male pathway through the development of immature testicular tissue), and through a genetic mutation, switched to the other reproductive pathway (in this case, the female pathway, through the development of genitalia involved in the large gamete reproductive role). This is called Complete Androgen Insensitivity Syndrome (CAIS), and it occurs in roughly 1 and 50,000 to 1 and 20,000 births—a rate of around 0.002 to 0.005%.[7]

Because affected individuals cannot respond to testosterone at any point in their life, regardless of treatment, they are unable to support the male reproductive role and develop a phenotype that is permanently structured around the female role (aside from the internal testes).

For Rebecca Helm and the other proponents of the sex spectrum, all this variation in sex development, from chromosomes, genetics, hormones, and receptors, means that male and female must not be objective biological categories and instead exist on a spectrum of traits from which we then arbitrarily divided people. But these categorical divisions of individuals into male or female are not arbitrary. While any deviation from the typical 46:XX female and typical 46:XY male is viewed as an exception to the supposed objectivity of the male and female categories by sex spectrum proponents, atypical cases reinforce the solidity of male and female once they are linked back to the two distinct roles in reproduction.

Males and females are not clusters of traits but rather two distinct reproductive strategies: the phenotype that produces small gametes and the phenotype that produces large gametes. Sex characteristics like chromosomes, gonads, hormones, and genitals are then organized in a sequential fashion around the functions of these two different roles.[8] Chromosomes hold the genes which differentiate the gonads, and the gonads release hormones which help develop the genitalia.

Atypical cases like 46:XX males, 46:XY females, 46:XX Congenital Adrenal Hyperplasia, 47:XXY Klinefelter syndrome, and 46:XY Complete Androgen Insensitivity Syndrome are all examples of genetic mutations within males and females, not new reproductive strategies. These conditions reveal the underlying mechanisms that orchestrate sex development. That orchestration is complex indeed, involving hundreds of unique genes and interacting networks, but the result is miraculously simple: production of males and females. However, this simple truth is purposefully ignored by sex spectrum proponents. Rebecca Helm obfuscates the reality of male and female by conflating variation in sex determination mechanisms and sex characteristics while detaching sex from the evolved system.

While her application of the sex spectrum's biological principle—*that sex is a continuum of characteristics between male and female*—sounds scientific and credible, the scientific language is simply a veneer for the social and political arguments hiding behind it. Evolutionary biologist Bret Weinstein calls this strategy *idea laundering:* portraying one's moral impulses, prejudices, and opinions as objective scientific knowledge.[9] Similar to a money laundering operation, which uses a legitimate business to hide the illegal activity underneath, idea laundering uses scientific language and credentials as a cover to sneak in sociopolitical agendas under the more legitimate veneer of 'science.'

At the end of Helm's thread, after she presents a variety of sex development conditions while portraying them as exceptions to male and female, she pivots into the social and political principles of the sex spectrum. She writes:

> Biological sex is complicated. Before you discriminate against someone on the basis of "biological sex" & identity, ask yourself: have you seen YOUR chromosomes? Do you know the genes of the people you love? The hormones of the people you work with? The state of their cells?
>
> Since the answer will obviously be no, please be kind, respect people's right to tell you who they are, and remember that you don't have all the answers. Again: biology is complicated. Kindness and respect don't have to be.

Helm is right that biology is complicated, but it can also be simple at the same time. The mechanisms that go into sex development are complex, yes, but the result is still male or female. In 99.98% of births, sex can be identified through quick observation of external genitalia;[10] in the remaining 0.02%, an infant's sex can be determined by analyzing multiple biological markers, such as genitalia, karyotype, hormonal profile, and gonadal tissue in reference to the role those traits play in reproduction.[11]

Should we be decent to others? Of course. Should we be accepting of people who have bodies that do not look like ours? Indeed. Should people be able to identify as they see fit in their personal lives? That too. However, acknowledging these truths does not mean material reality, such as the differences in people's bodies, can always be ignored, deconstructed, or denied. Boundaries are important, and respect requires them, whether it is boundaries between the sexes in physical competitive sports and vulnerable spaces, or boundaries between differing systems of belief, such as your right to identify how you feel (regardless of biology) and the other's right to not participate.

Even though Rebecca Helm may very well have good intentions, her sex spectrum argument is not helpful to those it claims to be for, because it conflates sex development conditions (DSDs) with those who identify as the opposite sex; alienates those with DSDs as not male or female; and obfuscates the biology of sex for social and political purposes, detaching sex from its role in reproduction.

The truth is we can teach others about the biology of male and female, and protect people's boundaries, while still being understanding to those who have developmental conditions or who identify as trans. There is no need for any idea laundering.

SUMMARY

- Sex is not found in a singular trait but in a systems view of biology: how characteristics are organized together into a functional system. In humans and most other complex species, sex characteristics are organized together into two and only two systems: male and female. Primary sex characteristics (like gonads and genitals) and secondary sex characteristics (like breasts or facial hair) follow from this fundamental difference.
- There is variation in anatomy and physiology within males and within females (as seen in typical variation and those with developmental conditions), but not a spectrum of sex.
- While sex development can be complex in humans, the result is simple: male or female. We can be decent and respectful to others, and accepting of those with atypical body types, but this also involves being respectful of people's boundaries, safety, and rights.

CHAPTER REFERENCES

1. Adrião, M., et al. (2020). 46:XX male disorder of sexual development. *Clinical Pediatric Endocrinology, 29(1), 43-45.*
2. Nistal, M., et al. (2019). Disorder of sex development, 46, XY pure gonadal dysgenesis. *Encyclopedia of Pathology, 1-3.*
3. Witchel, S. (2017). Congenital adrenal hyperplasia. *Journal of Pediatric and Adolescent Gynecology, 30(5),* 520-534.
4. Bearelly, P., et al. (2019). Recent advances in managing and understanding Klinefelter Syndrome. *F1000Research, 8(F1000 Faculty Reviews), 112.*
5. Hanna, E., et al. (2019). The lived experience of Klinefelter Syndrome: a narrative review of the literature. *Frontiers in Endocrinology, 10(825).*
6. Taplin, C., et al. (2009). Disorders of sexual differentiation: How do infants with complete androgen insensitivity syndrome present? In: *Endocrine Secrets (Fifth Edition).* 106; Lanciotti, L., et al. (2019). Different clinical presentations and management in complete androgen insensitivity syndrome (CAIS). *International Journal of Environmental Research and Public Health, 16(7).*
7. NIH. (2020). Androgen insensitivity syndrome. *MedlinePlus Genetics.*
8. Lehtonen, J. (2021). The legacy of Parker, Baker, and Smith 1972: gamete competition, the evolution of anisogamy, and model robustness. *Cells, 10(573).*
9. Boghossian, P. (2019). 'Idea laundering' in academia. *Wall Street Journal.*
10. Sax, L. (2002). How common is intersex? A response to Anne Fausto-Sterling. *The Journal of Sex Research, 39(3).*
11. Leon, N., Reyes, A., Harley, V. (2019). Differences of sex development: the road to diagnosis. *Lancet Diabetes Endocrinology, 7(7),* 1-15.

ARGUMENT 4

"THERE ARE MORE THAN TWO HUMAN SEXES"

SCISHOW, YOUTUBE

The title of this piece by SciShow is meant to make a provocative statement, and it is hard to argue they failed. No other sex spectrum video has as many views as this one by Hank Green and his team at SciShow—a popular science education channel on YouTube. It is now shared by sex spectrum proponents as 'proof' that sex is a spectrum, and that male and female are social constructs.

Of course, the statement 'there are more than two sexes in humans' is a false one. According to biology, sexes are phenotypes that produce two differently-sized gamete types (sperm or eggs), a definition you will not find mentioned in the SciShow video.

In humans and most other complex species across the plant and animal kingdoms, there are exactly two of these sexes.[1 2 3] Biologically, the female sex is the phenotype that produces few large sessile gametes (eggs), and the male sex is the phenotype that produces many small motile gametes (sperm).[4]

One scientific reason why the biological definition of the sexes matters is that it provides biologists with a way to reliably differentiate between male and female across, not just humans, but all anisogamous species despite the diversity in body types and behavior.[5] It therefore has beautiful simplicity and predictive power. If the meaning of "sexes" is that simple, how does SciShow argue against it? The answer is by using the complexity of sex development and the variation in people's bodies to muddy the reality of male and female. What follows is a series of conflations and obfuscations about sexes and human sex development.

ANALYSIS

The premise of SciShow's argument is that there is a continuum of traits between male and female (the biological principle) and that sex is defined by a mix of chromosomes, hormones, gonads, and genitals (the detachment of sex from reproduction). According to Green, any mismatch of these traits provides a contradiction to the categories of male and female, showing there is no single trait differentiating the sexes (the social principle). He argues this by using people with disorders of sex development as supposed exceptions to male and female.

To setup the premise that male and female are a continuum of traits, Green begins with a strawman: that scientists thought male and female were fundamentally defined by XY and XX. He says:

> In high school biology, we usually learn that the sexes in humans are fixed and concrete. Whether you are male or female is black-and-white and rooted in your DNA: your 23rd pair of chromosomes is either two X chromosomes or an X and a Y. That's it. End of story. And that's essentially what scientists thought, too.

The argument is a strawman because scientists who studied the biology of sex never thought male and female were defined by chromosomes, nor did they think the discovery of chromosomes was the "end of the story." Chromosomes were only discovered in 1882,[6] the Y chromosome in 1905,[7] and the sex-determining region Y gene (SRY) in 1990.[8] [9] Scientists, and especially biologists, already understood what male and female were well before any of these discoveries. In fact, the only reason they could identify chromosomes like X and Y as sex chromosomes, or the SRY gene as a "male" sex determining gene, is because they already had a concept of male and female independent of these systems. Thus, while male and female became associated with certain chromosomes, they are not and never were chromosomes. While chromosomes include the genes that determine the development path a fetus will go down, and thus, their sex, chromosomes are not the defining feature of male and female. They simply hold the genetic mechanisms that lead to male or female development.

So, if chromosomes are not the defining feature of the sexes, what definition of "sex" does Green provide? His answer is found in the first strategy of the sex spectrum's biological principle: sex is simply a mix of independent traits detached from reproduction. Green says:

> ...what we are talking about today is your biology, including your chromosomes, your hormones, your gonads, and your genitals.

Instead of describing what sex is, Green describes the various characteristics associated with sex: chromosomes, gonads, genitals, and hormones. Thus, a definition of sex is constructed around variation in what people's bodies look like, leaving his audience with a surface-level understanding. Rather than explaining how these traits play essential roles in the reproductive functions of the two sexes, Green leaves out reproduction completely by never defining male and female. In Green's argument, male and female are simply a specific cluster of chromosomes, hormones, gonads, and genitals. Any mismatch with this alignment provides evidence against male and female being reliable categories, or as Green says:

> ...these biological features don't always agree with each other. And they certainly don't always conform to those high school health class diagrams that tell us there is a single, universally correct pathway to being male and female.

Green is correct when he says these biological features do not always align (true), and there is no single pathway for developing as a male or female (also true), but there is a difference between having many pathways for developing as a male or female and being male or female. There are indeed many ways to develop as a male or female, with variation in anatomy and physiology, but there are still only two reproductive endpoints in human sex development: male or female.

However, since Green has constructed a non-universal definition of sex around various traits, and detached these traits from reproduction, he is able to use cases where they do not always align as supposed exceptions to male and female, beginning with the common conflation of chromosomes with sexes. He says:

> Sometimes, the chromosomes don't split into exact sets of 23—and that means there are a whole bunch of possible combinations of Xs and Ys that a person can end up with. For instance, people can inherit three Xs or an X and two Ys. These folks are normally taller than average. Those with three Xs have slender builds, and sometimes have minor learning disorders. The people who have an X and two Ys, on the other hand, tend to have more acne because of the extra testosterone in their systems. In both cases, people retain full fertility. Then, there's Turner syndrome, which happens when you get just one X.

As Green explained, if male and female are traditionally viewed as XY and XX, respectively, then people who are not XY or XX must not be male or female. The problem with this view is that it ignores what the sexes are. While someone's chromosome constitution may be different than what is expected, such as XXY or XXX, using the biological definition of sex helps us understand whether these individuals are male or female.

For example, those with three X chromosomes (XXX) develop the phenotype that produces eggs.[10] Those with XXY (SRY) develop the phenotype that produces sperm.[11] Those with XYY (SRY) also develop the phenotype that produces sperm.[12] And those with one X chromosome and no Y develop the phenotype that produces eggs.[13] All these disorders result in males or females because genetic sex determination in mammals is binary: the genetic networks within the chromosomes result in males or females regardless of how many sex chromosomes you add or remove.

When understood in the context of reproduction, integrating an understanding of biology as systems, male and female are clearly defined and not made unreliable by developmental anomalies. As stated previously, atypical development reinforces male and female by revealing the underlying mechanisms that produce the two sexes.

Let's explore some more examples Green describes as supposed exceptions to male and female. Mosaicism is one, where a fetus may develop with some cells containing XX and other cells containing XY. If severe enough, this can result in a disorder of sex development, causing underdeveloped reproductive organs and sometimes a mixing of typical male and female reproductive traits.

Mosaicism does not mean that someone is both male and female, or some percentage of male and another percentage of female. It just means they have a patchwork of genetically different cells. Their sex is still defined by their role in reproduction. Even in rare cases of mosaicism, where a person may develop a mix of traits associated with both sexes (such as internal ovarian and testicular tissue), the person does not actually embody both roles. When fertile, they can only fulfill one of the two.[14] Most cases of mosaicism, however, develop clearly defined male or female reproductive roles. For example, a mosaic woman, with a predominant 46:XY karyotype and a cell line of 45:X in her ovaries, was fertile and gave birth.[15] She is female because she developed a phenotype organized around eggs, regardless of her mosaicism.

Another set of examples used by Green involve disorders of sex development which are caused by translocations and mutations of important genes, resulting in a person whose body develops opposite of what is expected from the chromosomes.

For example, 46:XY individuals can develop as females from an over-expression of the ovarian transcription factor WNT4, and they are females because they develop the phenotype that produces eggs.[16] 46:XX individuals can develop as males from a translocation of the SRY gene onto an X chromosome, or an over-expression of the downstream target of SRY, a gene known as SOX9. They are males because they develop the phenotype that produces sperm.[17] And 46:XY individuals with the SRY gene can develop as females when the X chromosome is mutated, not allowing any androgen reception.[18] What these examples of sex development conditions reinforce is that, rather than showing there are more than two sexes, there are complex genetic pathways to arrive at one of the two endpoints: male or female.

One of the most common sex development disorders, and one used by Green as another supposed exception to male and female, is Congenital Adrenal Hyperplasia (CAH) in 46:XX females. CAH results in an underproduction of cortisol and an overproduction of androgens. Overproducing androgens can impact genitalia, a region highly sensitive to androgen exposure.

In 46:XX females, this can cause enlargement of the clitoris and sometimes fusion of the labia in a typical female who has ovaries, a Müllerian structure, and a vagina. Women with CAH are females because they develop the phenotype that produces eggs, and most are still fertile and can give birth.[19] Knowing this, see how Green describes these unambiguous females:

> …the overproduction of androgens can lead to external male genitalia paired with internal female gonads in people with XX chromosomes.

This is false. Females with CAH never develop male genitalia. While the clitoris and penis are homologous structures, in that they share a similar embryonic origin like the ovaries and testes, the two organs are not interchangeable. It does not matter how much androgen the female receives: the clitoris will not turn into a penis, and the labia will not turn into a scrotum with testes. A clitoris does not have the structure of a penis (you cannot urinate through it, unless you're a hyena), nor does the labia have the structure of a scrotum.

By claiming women with CAH can have external male genitalia, Green makes it seem like these females develop a penis and testicles on the outside, while having a vagina and ovaries on the inside. In reality, females with CAH are unambiguously female, with ovaries, a Müllerian structure, a vagina, and a vulva.

Green's claim that an enlarged clitoris constitutes "external male genitalia" is another example of how people with medical conditions are continually othered by proponents of the sex spectrum who do not understand the difference between biological systems (such as male and female) and bodily variation within the systems (diversity of body shape within males and females).

Finally, Green discusses the reality of genital mutilation, where the bodies of infants with incredibly rare disorders of sex development were surgically altered for prejudicial rather than medical reasons. Unnecessary surgery often caused gender dysphoria, mental health issues, and sexual dysfunction as patients grew up. But it was not that doctors did not know the infant's sex—that was usually obvious—it was that parents and doctors did not feel comfortable raising a child who looked different than other boys and girls, whether it was a boy with an underdeveloped penis or a girl with an enlarged clitoris.

The irony of the sex spectrum and Green's view is that, while it claims to champion the wide variation in body types, it stigmatizes and others those with atypical bodies by categorizing them as neither male nor female. Thus, rather than reducing genital mutilation, its principles increase the chances. This is because it believes those with atypical bodies are not male or female and that moving along the sex spectrum simply requires a change in how one's body looks. Logically, this implies that cosmetic surgery can "fix" traits deemed undesirable and move one to another category. For example, by labeling a larger clitoris in girls with CAH as "male genitalia," Green others their body, rather than accepting it as an example of a congenital disorder within females. This leads to the idea that girls with CAH are somehow "in between" male and female, and that surgically altering their body will move them along the spectrum. These are the consequences of what happens when sex is reduced to "what bodies look like" rather than "what reproductive function bodies serve."

All these variations and medical conditions have one purpose for Hank Green and SciShow: an elaborate smokescreen to obscure the simple fact that there are only two sexes in humans and most other complex species. Variation in body type and congenital reproductive conditions do not change the biological reality of male and female nor prove they are unreliable categories.

In the end Green does not actually claim there are more than two sexes in humans, as the title of the video suggests, but he does conclude with the sex spectrum's social principle: that there are no criteria that will consistently and reliably sort people into the categories of male and female. This of course is founded on the assumption that there is a continuum of characteristics between male and female (the sex spectrum biological principle). For Hank Green, this means that when it comes to knowing whether a person is male or female, there is no reliable method. And perhaps this supposed arbitrary categorization should be abandoned.

After all, if the sexes are simply constructed categories (the sex spectrum social principle), then why are we still using them to divide things based on sex, like restrooms or organized sports? Perhaps it would be better if we let people decide who they want to be (the sex spectrum political principle). Encapsulated in the final statement of the SciShow video is an application of all three principles:

> ...from clothes to restrooms to organized sports, they are raised in a society that is set up around a binary that just isn't binary. But researchers are thinking about how we can make our overall discussions and understanding of sex even more inclusive—and more

> accurate. Because even though biological sex may seem like one of those things that is relatively straightforward in a very, very complicated world, it's not!

The truth is that, while the mechanisms regulating sex development are complex, the endpoint is incredibly simple: production of males or females. This system is so clear that 99.98% of births can be accurately identified as male or female by quick observation of external genitalia.[20] The sex of the remaining 0.02% of births, often involving infants whose genitalia looks under masculinized for a male or over-masculinized for a female, is determined by analyzing five factors of sex development: genes, gonadal tissue (the gamete making factories), and the internal and external genitalia (the gamete transport systems).[21] The sex of the fetus is identified once these factors are analyzed in accordance with psychosocial well-being, sexual function, and future fertility.

To put the numbers in perspective, as evolutionary biologist Colin Wright notes, a rate of 0.02% is roughly the same chance that a flipped coin will land on its edge.[22] Even with the rarest and most extreme examples of congenital disorders, this makes sex one of the most reliable category systems in all of biology.

Denying the reality of sex helps no one. And it certainly does not help those with severe reproductive conditions to use their physical bodies and experiences for one's own social and political ideology. While SciShow's claim that there are "more than two human sexes" is never substantiated in the video, Green's conflation of human variation and medical conditions with additional sexes does much more harm than good, spreading pseudoscientific beliefs about male and female while othering those with medical conditions in the process.

SciShow is correct when they describe the existence of these various conditions of sex development, but they are incorrect when they attempt to prove these conditions represent additional sexes or that male and female are unreliable categories. By hiding behind the complexities of sex development and variation in sex characteristics without explaining how these systems work together for reproduction,

Hank Green leaves his viewers with a sloppy understanding of sex as "what my body looks like." SciShow would do well by integrating a systems biology perspective, where sexes are understood not through surface-level appearances but within the holistic functions they serve.

SUMMARY

- One's sex is universally defined by gamete type and identified by the structures that produce and release either gamete. Because there are only two gamete types in humans, there are only two sexes in humans—male and female.
- Sex characteristics (chromosomes, gonads, hormones, and genitals) are not the defining feature of sex, and they are not independent. Chromosomes hold the genes which determine the gonads, and the gonads produce hormones which build the genitalia. These characteristics are part of the reproductive system that supports one's sex. They are tightly dependent.
- Traits that can be plotted on a continuous x-axis, such as hormone levels, form a spectrum within males and within females. But this variation does not form new sexes. It reveals variation within each sex.
- We can be inclusive of people who have atypical bodies or who identify as the opposite sex, but this cannot come at the expense of other people's health, safety, and rights.

CHAPTER REFERENCES

1. Parker, GA., Baker, RR., Smith, VG., et al. (1972). The origin and evolution of gamete dimorphism and the male-female phenomenon. *Journal of Theoretical Biology, 36*, 529-553.
2. Czaran, T., Hoekstra. R. (2004). Evolution of sexual asymmetry. *BMC Evolutionary Biology, 4(34).*
3. Epelman, M., et al. (2005). Anisogamy, expenditure of reproductive effort, and the optimality of having two sexes. *Operations Research, 53(3).*
4. Lehtonen, J., Parker, G. (2014). Gamete competition, gamete limitation, and the evolution of two sexes. *Molecular Human Reproduction, 20(12).*
5. Schärer, L. (2017). The varied ways of being male and female. *Molecular Reproduction & Development, 84.*
6. Rudge, D.W. (2006). The man who invented the chromosome. Heredity, 97(136).
7. Brush, S.G. (1978). Nettie M. Stevens and the discovery of sex determination by chromosomes. *Isis, 69(2)*, 163-172.
8. Sinclair, A. (2001). Eleven years of sexual discovery. *Genome Biology, 2(7).*
9. Kashimada, K., Koopman, P. (2010). Sry: the master switch in mammalian sex determination. *Development, 137.*
10. Otter, M., et al. (2010). Triple X syndrome: a review of the literature. *European Journal of Human Genetics, 18(3)*, 265-271.
11. Bonomi, M., et al. (2017). Klinefelter syndrome (KS): genetics, clinical phenotype, and hypogonadism. *Journal of Endocrinological Investigation, 40(2)*, 123-134.
12. NIH. (2022). 47,XYY syndrome. *National Library of Medicine, Medline Plus.*
13. Cui, X, et al. (2018). A basic understanding of Turner syndrome: incidence, complications, diagnosis, and treatment. *Intractable & Rare Diseases Research, 7(4)*, 223-228.
14. Rosenfield, K. (2018). Hermaphrodite. *Encyclopedia of Animal Cognition and Behavior.*
15. Dumic, M., et al. (2008). Report of fertility in a woman with a predominantly 46,XY karyotype in a family with multiple disorders of sexual development. *The Journal of Clinical Endocrinology and Metabolism, 93(1)*, 182-189.

16. Jordan, B., et al. (2001). Up-regulation of WNT-4 signaling and dosage-sensitive sex reversal in humans. *American Journal of Human Genetics, 68,* 1102-1109.
17. Vorona, E., et al. (2007). Clinical, endocrinological, and epigenetic features of the 46,XX male syndrome, compared with 47,XXY Klinefelter patients. *Journal of Clinical Endocrinology & Metabolism, 92(9),* 3458-3465.
18. Oakes, M., et al. (2008). Complete androgen insensitivity syndrome: a review. *Journal of Pediatric and Adolescent Gynecology, 21(6).*
19. Mnif, M. Kamoun, M., Kacem, F., et al. (2013). Reproductive outcomes of female patients with congenital adrenal hyperplasia due to 21-hydroxylase deficiency. *Indian J Endocrinol Metab, 17(5),* 790-793.
20. Sax, L. (2002). How common is intersex? A response to Anne Fausto-Sterling. *The Journal of Sex Research, 39(3).*
21. Leon, N., Reyes, A., Harley, V. (2019). Differences of sex development: the road to diagnosis. *Lancet Diabetes Endocrinology, 7(7),* 1-15.
22. Murray, D., Teare, S. (1993). Probability of a tossed coin landing on edge. *Physical Review E (Statistical Physics, Plasmas, Fluids, and Related Interdisciplinary Topics), 48(4),* 2547-2552.

ARGUMENT 5

"SEX AND SENSIBILITY"

FORREST VALKAI, YOUTUBE

Imagine you are trying to win a debate, and instead of presenting your argument with relevant evidence, you gather an incredible amount of irrelevant data against your opponent's position. This is common with young earth creationists, who believe that the earth was created 6,000 years ago. To validate their beliefs, young earth creationists dump an incredible number of arguments onto the opponent. For example, they argue that the light coming from other stars was created in transit to make the appearance of age, or that radiometric dating and other objective methods of dating rocks and fossils are based on a host of incorrect assumptions.[1] Some of these arguments seem complex (and they might be), yet they are all irrelevant, misinterpretations of the evidence, or just complete fabrications. The key is that they all take advantage of people's ignorance.

This is known as the gish-gallop. It is a fallacy often found in pseudoscience, where you attempt to drown your opponent in a "flood of individually weak arguments" which take much energy to refute.[2] While it was and still is common with young earth creationists, the strategy is now being used by sex spectrum pseudoscientists.

The best example of this gish-gallop is "Sex and Sensibility," a 30 minute video that argues male and female are unreliable categories. It is written and presented by evolutionary anthropology student Forrest Valkai. Practically every sentence is riddled with information about the biology of sex, from the simple to the complex. Some points are true, and others are complete misrepresentations. There are so many points of information that it would take hours to carefully respond to each one, something we painstakingly did.[3]

Forrest's argument strategy is not much different from that of young earth creationists. Ironic, considering he is best known for debunking none other than young earth creationists. To try and overwhelm the viewer with irrelevant evidence, Forrest barrages the audience with biological information, showing the various genetics, anatomies, and behaviors between males and females in humans and across species. Using this information dump, he attempts to show that the two sexes are arbitrary. However, his argument relies on the constant conflation of diversity in genes, anatomy, and behavior with sexes. No well-studied biologist would argue that, for male and female to exist, they must have consistent genetic systems, anatomies, or behaviors across all species.

In biology, the two sexes are defined as the phenotypes that produce either the smaller gamete (sperm) or the larger gamete (eggs).[4] They are universal across the plant and animal kingdoms, having evolved independently in nearly every lineage of multicellular species.[5] Within this system of two, there is no constraint on the diversity of anatomy and behavior across species.[6] This is the beauty of the binary.[7]

Knowing this universal definition is enough to defeat Forrest's gish-gallop, because it can be correctly applied to all of his examples on the biology of sex. As an educational tool, let's analyze the examples he uses and show how they reinforce the two sexes. I've broken them into six categories:

1. Variation in sex allocation
2. Variation in gamete size
3. Variation in sex determination mechanisms
4. Variation in genetic networks
5. Variation in sex characteristics
6. Variation in sexual behavior

1. VARIATION IN SEX ALLOCATION

Sex allocation is the optimal allocation of male and female sexes to organisms, whether they are composed in the same individual or in separate individuals, and whether the proportion of males versus females is higher, lower, or equal.[8] The exact form of this allocation depends on the species and the environment. Forrest argues that the definition of sex is unreliable because of this diversity in sex allocation, that they can be composed in so many ways across species. He uses examples known as *dioecious, monoecious, simultaneous hermaphroditism*, and *sequential hermaphroditism.*

DIOECIOUS

This applies to a male-female sexual system in plants where individual plants are either male or female.[9] This means that one plant will have all female flowers or all male flowers.

MONOECIOUS

Forrest claims that monoecious refers to species with one sex. But this is wrong. Monoecious describes sexual systems in plants where a single plant has separate male and female flowers.[10] It does not mean one sex. It means *two sexes on one plant.* In other words, the individual plant has two sexes. This is where he shows that he misunderstands the meaning of dioecious and monoecious. The suffix *-ecious* describes the arrangement of sexual organs.

SIMULTANEOUS HERMAPHRODITISM

Sexual systems where male and female exist in the same individual (an individual produces both sperm and eggs). This is common in plants, where an individual plant has individual flowers with male and female sexes, known as perfect flowers.[11] It is also seen in slugs, where an individual is both male and female at the same time.

SEQUENTIAL HERMAPHRODITISM

Sexual systems where individuals switch sex depending on environmental circumstances. One example of this is the clownfish. They are born male but can switch sex if there is an absence of a female in the environment. Environmental triggers change the gonads from testes to ovaries, and they go from producing sperm to producing eggs.[12]

GONOCHORISM

Sexual system in 95% of animal species, including humans, where individuals are either male or female through their entire life.[13] [14] [15]

Rather than showing the meaning of sexes is arbitrary, the diversity of sex allocation reveals the many ways the male and female sexes can be composed across species. The only way we can know whether an organism is either male or female, or male and female, or having switched from male to female, is whether they have a phenotype that produces sperm or eggs, or a phenotype that produces both, or a phenotype that has switched from producing sperm to producing eggs.

2. VARIATION IN GAMETE SIZE

Forrest claims that the gamete size definition of the sexes does not work because there are some male-female species that have many different gamete sizes and huge sperm, and species with no gamete size.

SPECIES WITH MANY DIFFERENT GAMETE SIZES

Drosophila bifurca, a species of fruit fly, has one size of egg and three different sizes of sperm. Forrest claims this species should have four sexes. Here's the problem: he's missing the fundamental meaning of "sexes."

When biologists say the sexes are defined by the difference in gamete size, this is a shorthand for what the size differences represent. The size differences represent the two different contributions in sexual reproduction.[16] Males produce the gamete that holds far less to no resources for the future zygote, like a payload, which fertilizes the resource-heavy egg produced by the female.

When the sexes were first evolving over one billion years ago, there was an evolutionary trade-off between producing many small, fast gametes with little to no cellular resources and producing few large, slow gametes with most of the resources for the zygote.[17]

It does not matter whether there are many different sizes of sperm within a species or across species, nor does it matter whether there are many different sizes of egg. What matters is the contribution to reproduction, the organism providing the sperm to fertilize the egg or the organism providing the egg to be fertilized by the sperm. The size difference between the male and female gametes is a great way to distinguish the sexes. In the fruit fly, the three different types of males can be defined as male because they all produce the sperm (the fertilizer).

HUGE SPERM

Forrest also claims that the gamete size distinction is violated because the same fruit fly produces sperm that is bigger than the female's egg. The definition is not violated because this large sperm still fertilizes the egg and contributes little to no resources for the zygote. But why is the sperm bigger? It's actually not bigger in volume; its head is still far smaller than the female's egg. It's just that the sperm is bigger in length. The male fruit fly has sperm that is 20 times the length of its body.[18] It's a wound up ball of string that unravels inside the female reproductive tract. Biologists think its immense length is due to a process called runaway sexual selection, where male to male competition is so strong that sperm length was selected for by the female fruit flies as an indicator for male quality.[19]

Longer sperm can also displace competitor sperm inside the female's reproductive tract. Female fruit flies have large seminal receptacles, and so the energy cost for such long sperm is outweighed by the increased likelihood of fertilization with high quality sperm. Thus, it is the female reproductive tract that, in part, drove the shape of the male's sperm. A similar situation happens in mammals where the longer the fallopian tube length is in the females of a given species, the larger the testes will be in the males.[20]

What variation in gamete size teaches us is the expected diversity of sperm and eggs, not that the sex divide is arbitrary. Even with sperm and egg variation, we define them as sperm versus eggs by the two different functional contributions in reproduction.

SPECIES WITH NO GAMETE SIZE

Forrest claims the gamete size definition for sexes is problematic because there are species who have male and female sexes but their gametes are the same size. The biology literature is very clear that these are not male and female sexes. They are called mating types.[21] And such species have no sexes. This unusual sexual system is called isogamy, a more ancient form of sexual reproduction often found in fungi or algae where gametes are the same size and form. They contribute equally to the zygote, as opposed to anisogamous (male-female) systems, where the cellular contribution to the zygote is unequal.

No biology literature claims that species with isogamy have male and female sexes, because sexes imply anisogamy (differently sized gametes) and mating types imply isogamy (same sized gametes).[22] Isogamous gametes are only different on the molecular level, regulating which gametes can fuse with other gametes.[23] These molecular regulators act as lock and key systems, where certain gamete types can only successfully fuse with their pair. There can be thousands or tens of thousands of gamete types in isogamous species. But no experienced biologist claims these are sexes. For mating types to be sexes, they would require a difference in size and behavior between the gametes.

What isogamy teaches us is that there was a more ancient form of sexual reproduction before male and female originated, where gametes were not differentiated, but it does not call into question what male and female are, because isogamy is an entirely different sexual system.

3. VARIATION IN SEX DETERMINATION MECHANISMS

Sex determination mechanisms are the regulatory systems, genetic and environmental, that determine sex, a technical term in biology for the development decision that triggers development down the male or female path in the womb.[24] Sex determination mechanisms answer the mechanistic question of "how does an individual organism become a male or female?"[25]

These mechanisms reveal how the genetic, hormonal, and environmental systems work together to build the male and female systems. Across species, there are many systems for developing an individual's sex.[26] But Forrest claims this diversity in sex determination mechanisms shows sex is a spectrum, using two examples.

Z-W SYSTEM IN BIRDS

Unlike mammals, birds use the Z-W chromosomal system to determine sex, where ZZ birds develop into males, and ZW birds develop into females.[27] How do we know that the males are ZZ and the females are ZW? Could it be due to the biological definition of sex? The gamete type they contribute in reproduction?

TEMPERATURE SEX DETERMINATION

Reptiles are unique in the animal kingdom in that many species determine sex by the temperature at which their eggs incubate. In crocodiles, for instance, a certain range of temps trigger development into a male and another range triggers development into a female.[28]

The fact these species of reptile do not have sex chromosomes like us yet still develop as either male or female should indicate there is a difference between the mechanisms that determine sex (genes, temperature) and sex itself. If sex determination mechanisms were sex, then with temperature sex determination, each temp value would be its own sex. Crocodiles would have infinite sexes! But they do not, because sex determination mechanisms are different from "sexes."

4. VARIATION IN GENETIC NETWORKS

Forrest also argues that, because there are so many genes and potential pathways for developing into a male or female, the two sexes cannot be reliably defined. This conflates gene networks with sexes.

GENES FOR MAKING TESTES AND OVARIES

Developing into a male or female in mammals requires a complex genetic network.[29] As Forrest correctly points out, we technically have all the genes required for developing testes versus ovaries, because almost all of the genes involved in sex differentiation of the gonads are located on the autosomes (non sex chromosomes).

Some genes promote testes development, and other genes promote ovarian development. However, these genes are mutually antagonistic.[30] [31] [32] Their expression blocks the opposite-sex pathway from being expressed. Male-making genes suppress female-making genes, and female-making genes suppress male-making genes.

For example, the SRY gene on the male Y chromosome upregulates SOX9, which differentiates the gonads into testes. The upregulation of SOX9 then inhibits female-making genes like WNT4 from being expressed. Females do not have the SRY gene, and so WNT4 is able to suppress SOX9, and ovaries develop.[33] The purpose of this mutually antagonistic system is to guarantee that both genetic networks do not activate at the same time, which would most often result in infertility.[34]

SEX REVERSAL IN MICE

Forrest uses experimental genetic tests on XX and XY mice, where researchers removed or added sex determining genes during *in utero* development, resulting in a phenomenon called sex reversal.[35]

Sex reversal occurs when the sexual trajectory of the gonad is changed to the opposing pathway, switching the sexual phenotype of the organism from what is expected by their chromosomes. For example, XX mice with loss of WNT4 and FOXL2 developed into males, and

XY mice without the upregulation of SOX9 developed into females. This happened during the critical window of gonadal differentiation before it is fully established, not after.[36]

But how do we define the sex of these XX males and XY female mice? Answer: by their gonad/gamete type. Gametes differentiate according to the gonad tissue environment, not the chromosomes.[37] [38] This is one reason why the sexes are defined by their reproductive role and not by chromosomes. These examples of sex reversal in fetal mice reveal the genetic mechanisms that control male and female development; they simply reinforce the two sexes.

WITHOUT GENETIC TESTS, WE CANNOT ASSUME

Forrest claims that without having your chromosomes tested or your genes analyzed, we have no idea where each of us land when it comes to our sex. This is not true. Karyotype studies have been conducted on tens of thousands of newborns across different decades, showing repeatedly that a person's reproductive system matches with what is expected from their chromosomes (XX develops as a female; XY develops as a male) in more than 99% of births.[39] [40] [41] Karyotypes outside of the typical XX and XY almost always result in infertility. And when people with these conditions are fertile, they produce sperm or eggs, never both and never a third gamete type. Thus, they are not additional sexes.

From genetic networks to chromosome combinations, it is odd Forrest thinks this variation proves male and female are arbitrary. On the contrary, these examples reinforce the meaning of male and female and reveal the mechanisms controlling their development.

5. VARIATION IN SEX CHARACTERISTICS

Forrest argues that an additional reason why the definition of sex is arbitrary is due to variation in sexual characteristics, such as genitalia or hormone levels, within humans and across species.

ARE WE BORN MALE OR FEMALE?

Forrest claims that the idea we are born male or female is deeply flawed, and that there are hermaphroditic species that are simultaneous (they produce both sperm and eggs) or sequential (they start out as one sex and then switch).

First, in humans, we can accurately and easily observe sex at birth or even in utero by observing external genitalia, which accurately correlates to sex in more than 99.98% of births.[42] [43] Second, what do hermaphroditic species have to do with humans, whose individuals are either male or female? And third, hermaphroditic species still involve only two sexes: male and female. It's just that they are composed in a single individual, where individuals are both male and female or can switch due to environmental circumstances.

In humans, there has been no documented case of a hermaphrodite. You will see medical literature sometimes using the term hermaphrodite applied to a human with a sex development disorder, but this is a misnomer. Since 2005, scientists have pushed to abandon the term hermaphrodite for humans, as it is "scientifically specious and clinically problematic."[44] The definition of a hermaphrodite is to develop both male and female systems and to be able to reproduce as both sexes. No case has been identified in any human.[45]

HYENAS AND THE PSEUDO-PENIS

Forrest uses the hyena, where its females have external genitalia similar looking to the males. This is supposed to confuse the viewer into thinking that the definition of sex is arbitrary. But the female hyena is female not because of the assumptions of biologists, but because she develops the phenotype that produces eggs.

Her 'penis-like' structure is actually a giant clitoris through which she urinates, copulates, and gives birth.[46] The female hyena shows the unique sex characteristics within females of other species.

MALE LACTATION IN A FRUIT BAT

In a Malaysian fruit bat species known as the Dayak fruit bat, the males of the species have been observed to produce milk. But their mammary glands and nipples were not as large as females, and the amount of milk was only about a tenth of that produced by females. Males were not observed nursing young.

What's the cause? One reason might be related to diet. These fruit bats eat fruit, but they also eat leaves that can contain estrogen-like compounds called phytoestrogens, which can stimulate milk production.[47] So, this ability for the males to produce milk could serve no functional purpose. Even if they lactated just like females, it would not call into question which bat is male versus which is female.

Forrest makes the fundamental error of conflating variation in sex characteristics within humans and across species with sex itself. But sex characteristics evolved from the two sexes. They are byproducts of the two sexes, not examples beyond them.

6. VARIATION IN SEXUAL BEHAVIOR

The last major category Forrest uses is variation in sexual behavior. He shows many cool examples of behavior across the animal kingdom and attempts to use this as evidence that male and female are arbitrary.

SEAHORSE REPRODUCTION

One major example Forrest uses is the unique reproductive biology of seahorses. Unlike mammals where the females gestate the young, male seahorses become "pregnant." Except this pregnancy is not like mammals. The female seahorse deposits her eggs into the "brood pouch" of the male, where the eggs are fertilized by his sperm and incubated, protected, and provisioned.[48] [49] Even though the male seahorse "gestates" the young in his brood pouch, he is defined as male because he develops the phenotype that produces the sperm, just like every other male across species.

DOMINANT FEMALES AND SUBMISSIVE MALES

Bonobos have dominant, socially aggressive females who form close bonds with each other to form social power over other group members. This goes against the stereotype of male aggression and domination over females, because there is evidence that these female bonds actually reduce male aggression patterns in the bonobo.[50] Furthermore, male bonobos tend to stay with their mothers through their lives, relying on them for protection against threats. As famous primatologist Frans De Waal writes, "The highest-ranking males of a bonobo community tend to be sons of important females."

Despite their unique sexual behavior, we define the bonobos as male or female by the phenotypes that produce sperm or eggs.

MALES BUILDING NESTS; FEMALES GETTING THE FOOD

In birds, it is common for the male to build the nest. There are many different techniques for nest building across avians; its ultimate purpose is to provide protection against environmental stress and predation which can also reduce offspring mortality and the need for parental care. Female birds have been sexually selected to seek out males with excellent nest building skills.

For example, in the common goby, whose males build nests underneath mussel shells by excavating a sand cavity, females prefer males with larger nests and solid sand ceilings.[51] We do not define them as male or female based on their behavior; we define them based on the biological definition of sex: the phenotype that produces sperm or eggs.

It is odd that Forrest thinks variation in sexual behavior across species is evidence that the male-female distinction is arbitrary. Instead of showing that male and female sexes are social constructs, the wide variation in sexual behavior reveals the beautiful diversity within males and females, something Forrest should appreciate if he truly wants to eliminate sex-based stereotypes and social expectations for the sexes.

CONFLATION OF DIVERSITY WITH SEXES

Ultimately, Forrest's constant theme throughout his 30 minute video is the conflation of diversity within male and female with male and female themselves. He uses this treasure-trove of biological facts about the diversity of sex-related traits across species and within humans as evidence that male and female are somehow arbitrary, social constructs, and that the definition does not stand up to scrutiny. But the biological definition of sexes is universal: it applies to every species with male-female sexes, regardless of within-species diversity in sexual behavior, sex characteristics, genetics, or sex allocation.[52] [53] It's not that every point Forrest utilizes is wrong; it's that these many biological facts are used incorrectly, misrepresented, or are completely fabricated.

Forrest's gish-gallop of irrelevant or misleading biological information is meant to confuse and muddy the viewer's knowledge of male and female, not broaden or strengthen it. Just like young earth creationists who rely on the reader's ignorance of physics and cosmology to be effective, Forrest Valkai relies on the viewer's ignorance of biology to be effective, which is no fault of their own. It just means they are being taken advantage of by someone who should know better.

If Forrest wants to be effective at communicating topics in biology while combating young earth creationism and its rampant denial of evolution, he should first confront his own.

SUMMARY

- Forrest conflates six categories of variation with sex: sex allocation, gamete size, sex determination mechanisms, genetic networks, sex characteristics, and sexual behavior.
- The biological definition of sex shows us that in all these categories, male and female can be consistently defined.
- Forrest's gish-gallop can be defeated by focusing on a common theme: how the sexes are universally defined in biology.

CHAPTER REFERENCES

1. Peppe, D.J. & Deino, A. L. (2013). Dating rocks and fossils using geologic methods. *Nature Education Knowledge, 4(10).*
2. Elsher, P. (n.d.). Gish gallop (logical fallacy): definition and examples. *Fallacy In Logic.*
3. Elliott, Z., Breheny, C. (2022). Biology of sex: detailed analysis of Forrest Valkai's Sex and Sensibility Video. *Paradox Institute, YouTube.*
4. Lehtonen, J., Parker, G. (2014). Gamete competition, gamete limitation, and the evolution of two sexes. *Molecular Human Reproduction, 20(12).*
5. Kirk, D. (2006). Oogamy: Inventing the sexes. *Current Biology, 16(24).*
6. Schärer, L. (2017). The varied ways of being male and female. *Molecular Reproduction & Development, 84.*
7. Goymann, W., Brumm, H., Kappeler, P. (2022). Biological sex is binary, even though there is a rainbow of sex roles. *BioEssays, 45(2).*
8. Schärer, L., Pen, I. (2013). Sex allocation and investment into pre- and post-copulatory traits in simultaneous hermaphrodites: the role of polyandry and local sperm competition. *Philosophical Transactions B, 368(1613).*
9. Muyle, A., et al. (2021). Dioecy is associated with high genetic diversity and adaptation rates in the plant genus Silene. *Molecular Biology and Evolution, 38(3),* 805-818.
10. de Jong, T., Shmida, A., Thuijsman, F. (2008). Sex allocation in plants and the evolution of monoecy. *Evolutionary Ecology Research, 10,* 1087-1109.
11. Avise, J. (2011). *Hermaphroditism: A primer on the biology, ecology, and the evolution of dual sexuality.* Columbia University Press.
12. Casas, L, Rey-Saborido, F., Ryu, T., et al. (2016). Sex change in clownfish: molecular insights from transcriptome analysis. *Scientific Reports, 6.*
13. Muyle, A., et al. (2021).
14. Holub, A., Shackelford, T. (2021). Gonochorism. *Encyclopedia of Animal Cognition and Behavior. Springer.*

15. Pla, S., Benvenuto, C., Capellini, I., et al. (2022). Switches, stability, and reversals in the evolutionary history of sexual systems in fish. *Nature Communications, 13.*
16. Lehtonen, J. (2017). Gamete Size. *Encyclopedia of Evolutionary Psychological Science.*
17. Lehtonen, J., Kokko, H., Parker, GA. (2016). What do isogamous organisms teach us about sex and the two sexes? *PTBS, 371(1706),* 1-12.
18. Gardiner, J. (2016). The bigger, the better. *Nature Evolution, 533(476).*
19. Hill, A., Eisenberg, D. (2016). The long and short of it: new insights on sperm length help demystify the complexities of sexual selection. *Asian Journal of Andrology, 18(6),* 902-903.
20. Anderson, M., Dixson, A., Dixson, A. (2006). Mammalian sperm and oviducts are sexually selected: evidence for co-evolution. *J Zool, 270,* 682–6.
21. Perrin, N. (2011). What uses are mating types? The developmental switch model. *Evolution, 66(4),* 947-956.
22. Ibid.
23. Lehtonen, J., Parker, G. (2014). Gamete competition, gamete limitation, and the evolution of two sexes. *Molecular Human Reproduction, 20(12).*
24. Eggers, S., Sinclair, A. (2012). Mammalian sex determination: Insights from humans and mice. *Chromosome Res, 20.*
25. Beukeboom, L, Perrin, N. (2014). *The evolution of sex determination.* Oxford, UK: Oxford University Press.
26. Bachtrog, D., Mank, J.E., Peichel, C.L., Kirkpatrick, M., Otto, S.P., Ashman, T.L., et al. (2014). Sex determination: Why so many ways of doing it? *PLoS Biol, 12(7).*
27. Ioannidis, J., et al. (2021). Primary sex determination in birds depends on DMRT1 dosage, but gonadal sex does not determine adult secondary sex characteristics. *PNAS, 118(10).*
28. Cornejo-Paramo, P., et al. (2020). Sex determination systems in reptiles are related to ambient temperature but not to the level of climatic fluctuation. *BMC Evolutionary Biology, 20(103).*
29. Eggers, S., Sinclair, A. (2012). Mammalian sex determination: Insights from humans and mice. *Chromosome Res, 20.*

30. Warr, N., et al. (2012). The molecular and cellular basis of gonadal sex reversal in mice and humans. *WIREs Dev Bio, 1.*
31. Bashamboo, A., et al. (2017). Anomalies in human sex determination provide unique insights into the complex genetic interactions of early gonad development. *Clinical Genetics, 91,* 143-156.
32. Witchel, S. (2018). Disorders of sex development. Best Practice and Research in Clinical Obstetrics and Gynecology, 48.
33. Leon, N., Reyes, A., Harley, V. (2019). Differences of sex development: the road to diagnosis. *Lancet Diabetes Endocrinology, 7(7),* 1-15.
34. Warr, N., et al. (2012).
35. Ottolenghi, C., et al. (2007). Loss of WNT4 and FOXL2 leads to female-to-male sex reversal extending to germ cells. *Human Molecular Genetics, 16(23),* 2795-804.
36. Weber, C. & Capel, B. (2018). Sex reversal. *Current Biology, 28(21),* R1234-R1236.
37. McClaren, A., et al. (1995). Germ cells and germ cell sex. *Phil Trans R Soc Lond B, 350,* 229-233.
38. Kocer, A., Reichmann, J., Best, D., Adams, I. (2009). Germ cell sex determination in mammals. *Molecular Human Reproduction, 15(4),* 205-213.
39. Maeda et al (1991). A cytogenetic survey of 14,835 consecutive liveborns. *The Japanese Journal of Genetics, 36(1),* 117-129.
40. Hamerton et al (1975). A cytogenetic survey of 14,069 newborn infants. I. Incidence of chromosome abnormalities. *Clinical Genetics, 8(4),* 223-243.
41. Nielsen & Sillesen (1975). Incidence of chromosome aberrations among 11,148 newborn children. *Human Genetics, 30(1),* 1-12.
42. Sax, L. (2002). How common is intersex? A response to Anne Fausto-Sterling. *The Journal of Sex Research, 39(3).*
43. van Zoest, M., et al. (2019). Sex assignment and diagnostics in infants with ambiguous genitalia: a single-center retrospective study. *Sexual Development, 13(3).*
44. Dreger, A., Chase, C., Sousa, A., et al. (2005). Changing the nomenclature-taxonomy for intersex: A scientific and clinical rationale. *Journal of Pediatric Endocrinology & Metabolism, 18,* 729-733.

45. Rosenfield, K. (2018). Hermaphrodite. *Encyclopedia of Animal Cognition and Behavior.*
46. Cunha, G., et al. (2005). The ontogeny of the urogenital system of the spotted hyena. *Biology of Reproduction, 73,* 554-564.
47. Houghton, M. (2023). The incredible milk-producing male bat. *Bat Conservation International.*
48. Zhang, H., et al. (2018). The roles of the kisspeptin system in the reproductive physiology of the lined seahorse (Hippocampus erectus), an ovoviviparous fish with male pregnancy. *Frontiers in Neuroscience, 12.*
49. Stolting, K. N., Wilson, A.B. (2007). Male pregnancy in seahorses and pipefish: beyond the mammalian model. *Bioessays, 29,* 884-896.
50. Clay, Z., Zuberbühler, K. (2012). Communication during sex among female bonobos: effects of dominance, solicitation, and audience. *Scientific Reports, 2.*
51. Pärssinen, V., et al. (2019). Male and female preferences for nest characteristics under paternal care. *Ecology and Evolution, 9(13),* 7780-7791.
52. Lehtonen, J., Parker, G. (2014). Gamete competition, gamete limitation, and the evolution of two sexes. *Molecular Human Reproduction, 20(12).*
53. Schärer, L. (2017). The varied ways of being male and female. *Molecular Reproduction & Development, 84.*

ARGUMENT 6

"SEX REDEFINED"

NATURE

Redefining the sexes requires the rejection of fundamental observations from biology, whether it is the universality of male and female as distinct reproductive functions to their differentiation and development in the womb. Sex spectrum proponents have found the most effective way to reject this evidence: take advantage of biology's complexity. Redefining the sexes uses complexity in biology to muddy the reality of male and female. No other piece employs this strategy better than Claire Ainsworth's "Sex Redefined." Published in Nature in 2015, the piece is the standard for how complex scientific findings can be employed for pseudoscientific political ideologies. Ainsworth explores a variety of rare medical conditions to prove that the "idea of two sexes is simplistic" and to deconstruct male and female. To fully analyze her argument and understand how to respond, let's explore the piece with research from evolutionary and developmental biology.

The first step is defining the sexes. There is no definition of male and female provided in "Sex Redefined," so for clarity, we must show the biological definition of male and female:

> **Universal biological definition**: The male sex is the phenotype that produces the smaller gametes (sperm), and the female sex is the phenotype that produces the larger gametes (eggs).[1]

The definition applies across all species that reproduce through gametes of differing size (anisogamy); it is therefore the universal biological definition for male and female. Ainsworth's piece "Sex Redefined" fails to provide this definition and any definition at all. Instead, she focuses on the variation in structure (phenotype) within males and females, detaching it from its relationship to function (gamete production). In other words, she looks at the appearance of people's bodies while never relating it to what sex-based function those structures serve. This allows her to claim that sex exists on a spectrum.

Like all common sex spectrum arguments, "Sex Redefined" detaches sex from its role in reproduction and uses complex medical conditions as tools to deconstruct male and female and replace these categories with subjective identity. This requires a fundamental redefinition of male and female from reproductive categories into mere mixtures of independent characteristics.

For most of the piece, Ainsworth utilizes the sex spectrum's biological principle (sex exists on a continuum between male and female) to argue that the categories of male and female are overly simplistic and need redefining. She does this by:

1. Detaching male and female from reproduction.
2. Using disorders of sex development as exceptions.
3. Conflating sex determination mechanisms with sex.

To analyze her argument, let's breakdown the examples she uses.

GENETICS

Advanced DNA sequencing has uncovered the wide range of gene variation that can impact people's bodies, both in typical individuals and in those with DSDs.

Ainsworth uses this genetic variation as her first tool in the sex spectrum arsenal by conflating the mechanisms that determine and develop sex with sex itself.

CASE 1
A PREGNANT WOMAN HAS AN UNUSUAL KARYOTYPE

In 2010, a pregnant woman visited a clinic at the Royal Melbourne Hospital in Australia to scan for chromosomal abnormalities. There she discovered her own chromosomal makeup was unusual: one set of her own cells carried 45:X, typical of Turner's Syndrome in females, and another set of her cells carried 46:XY, the typical for males. She had a mosaic karyotype.[2]

Ainsworth claims this case shows sex is more complicated than male or female. But this is a category error: conflating chromosomes with sex. The mother developed the large gamete phenotype, and she was pregnant with her third child; it is rather safe to say she's female. It therefore does not prove Ainsworth's point that the idea of "two sexes" is "simplistic." Does it show us that chromosomal abnormalities can occur? Yes. Does it show us the amazing world of genetics? Yes. But does it show us that male and female are unreliable categories? No. The fact that the patient is female, even with her unusual karyotype, simply reinforces the binary. So, why the confusion?

CASE 2
MISMATCH OF CHROMOSOMES AND PHENOTYPE

Ainsworth says, "Gene mutations affecting gonad development can result in a person with XY chromosomes developing typically female characteristics, whereas alterations in hormone signaling can cause XX individuals to develop along male lines." It is true that, rarely, males may develop with XX chromosomes and females may develop with XY chromosomes, opposite of what is expected from the chromosomes.[3]

But sex spectrum proponents interpret mismatch of chromosomes and phenotype as evidence of a spectrum between male and female. It's not. This is a conflation of sex determination mechanisms with sex. The only reason we can identify these individuals as male or female is because we already know what sexes are irrespective of chromosomes.

Males with XX chromosomes are male because they develop the small gamete phenotype, and females with XY chromosomes are female because they develop the large gamete phenotype.[4]

CASE 3
SEX DETERMINING GENE PATHWAYS

Ainsworth presents a variety of genes that, when moved onto different chromosomes, can change the development path of the fetus from what's expected by their chromosomes. These include the SRY and SOX9 genes for testes development and WNT4 and RSPO1 for ovarian development.[5]

First, take the SRY gene. It's the sex-determining region on the Y chromosome, and the master switch for male sex determination by initiating gonadal differentiation into testes.[6] Sometimes, however, SRY can translocate or mutate. Three examples show us how important this gene is for male sex differentiation and development:

- On very rare occasions, a fetus may develop with two X chromosomes and one Y, or three Xs and one Y, or even four Xs and one Y. Despite the extra X chromosomes, all these cases develop as males thanks to the presence of SRY on the Y chromosome.
- Sometimes, a translocation of the SRY gene results in it being placed on an X chromosome in a fetus with two X chromosomes. Thanks to the presence of SRY, the fetus develops as a male despite having no Y chromosome.
- In exceptional cases, a fetus may develop as a female with an XY karyotype. Because the SRY gene is absent, they develop as females.[7]

Second, take the WNT4 gene. WNT4 plays an essential role in promoting ovarian development. With a duplication of WNT4 in XY fetuses, testes development is suppressed by undermining the role of the SRY gene, inhibiting its downstream target, SOX9.[8] In its place, ovarian differentiation and development is promoted and the fetus develops as a female. Thus, cases of SRY or WNT4 mutation show us that sex development requires a precise sequence of activating and repressing factors. Alter this sequence, and the fetus may develop as the opposite sex compared to what is expected from the chromosomes.

Ainsworth presents these cases to try and claim that the idea of two sexes is simplistic, because the process of sex determination can be complex and variable. But whether it's through the activation or suppression of certain genes, or even mutations or translocations onto other chromosomes, these genetic networks produce incredibly simple results: males and females.

Because male and female sex determining genes are expressed antagonistically by inhibiting genes involved in the opposite sex path, such genes cannot promote both sex pathways at the same time.[9] Thus, cases of SRY and WNT4 translocation, mutation, or duplication have consistently resulted in males or females, not both nor in between.

HORMONES

Decades of research in biology has shown the importance of sex hormones for the development of the fetus. Androgens like testosterone and dihydrotestosterone play a major role in masculinizing the male fetus during sex development, building the internal and external genitalia. Testosterone builds the sperm transportation systems while dihydrotestosterone descends the testes into the scrotal sac and grows the penis. These structures will help carry and release sperm.

Alter this system, however, such as reducing the amount of testosterone or blocking its reception, and there will be atypical results. Ainsworth uses this diversity in hormonal profiles to claim that sex exists on a spectrum.

CASE 4
ANDROGEN INSENSITIVITY

Ainsworth uses a condition called Complete Androgen Insensitivity Syndrome to claim that sex exists on a spectrum. But a closer look at this condition shows us the importance of the androgen receptors for male sex development; it does not make the categories of male and female unreliable.

CAIS causes a 46:XY fetus to develop as a female despite having internal testicular tissue. A mutation in the androgen receptor gene on the X chromosome halts the body's ability to respond to testosterone produced from the testes. With no ability to respond to T, the testes do not develop further (remaining in the abdomen),[10] the germ cells never differentiate into sperm,[11] the primordial internal genitalia disintegrate, and the external genitalia develops into a vulva and lower vagina.[12] Testosterone produced by the testes is converted into estrogen, and the body feminizes.[13] Girls and women with CAIS usually do not develop fallopian tubes or a uterus because the testes produce anti-Müllerian hormone (AMH), and AMH causes these female structures to regress before they can develop further.

However, because the bodies of those with CAIS cannot respond to androgen, there are many consequences. First, they are infertile: they cannot produce sperm from their internal testicular tissue, and since they do not have ovaries, they cannot produce ova. Second, because of their phenotype determined by the AR gene mutation, they are observed at birth as females, raised as females, and even go through puberty as females (just without menstruation). Because of the absence of T reception and the conversion of the testosterone into estrogen, women with CAIS tend to have female-typical bone and muscle structures, develop breasts at puberty, and have female-typical psychological profiles, such as sexual attraction to males.

Ainsworth and sex spectrum proponents tend to believe that CAIS proves male and female are unreliable categories. But if male and female did not exist, CAIS would not exist. We can only understand such a condition because male and female are real, biological categories, produced by complex systems of genes and hormones which work together to form the two reproductive roles. CAIS does not call into question this system but rather shows us the underlying mechanisms (like testosterone and androgen receptors) that help produce the binary system of sex.

CASE 5
HORMONALLY-INDUCED GENITAL DISORDERS

Infants are sometimes born with congenital conditions that cause the external genitalia to look different than what's typical. Ainsworth brings up Congenital Adrenal Hyperplasia (CAH), a condition that affects both males and females.

In 46:XX females with CAH, a mutation in the CYP21A2 gene leads to an overproduction of androgens in the adrenal glands, and the female fetus, who develops ovaries, uterus, cervix, and vagina, is exposed to this higher level of androgens.[14]

Because the external genitalia is highly sensitive to androgen exposure, the clitoris and labia of the female fetus can look slightly masculinized (longer clitoris, fused labia).[15] This does not mean they are suddenly males, however. As discussed in this book's response to SciShow's video, "There Are More Than Two Human Sexes", girls and women with CAH are female because they develop the phenotype that produces eggs, not sperm.

The fact some genitalia look different from the norm does not mean that sex is a spectrum, that people can have both a penis and a vagina, or that sex can be changed through hormones. It simply means that, within males and within females, there are differences in the external appearance of genitalia, some differences from typical variation and others from disorders. Put simply, there is variation of sex characteristics, but not variation of sex.

Using women with CAH, or other people with developmental conditions, to argue that sex is a spectrum is not just scientifically inaccurate, but it also reinforces stereotyped ideals of male and female bodies. In the sex spectrum, if your genitalia is more masculinized for a female, you're suddenly not female or exist "in between" the sexes. For sex spectrum proponents who say they are against 'othering' people for being different, they should stop claiming people with atypical genital morphology are not males or females.

CASE 6
A UTERUS FOUND IN A FERTILE MALE

In the hormone category, Ainsworth concludes by mentioning a vanishingly rare case: a 70-year-old man who fathered children went to the hospital for a hernia, and the doctors discovered a uterus in his abdomen.[16] Sex spectrum proponents claim that this case proves sex is a spectrum, and that the categories of male and female are unreliable.

However, this male with a uterus did not develop the large gamete phenotype. Instead, he developed testes, internal sperm transportation systems, and a penis. Not only this, but he was fertile and fathered children with his sperm. So, why the uterus? The vestigial uterus had developed due to a gene mutation, causing anti-Müllerian hormone to not be fully produced, which allowed parts of the Müllerian structure to remain, leaving the vestigial uterus.[17]

This disorder is called Persistent Müllerian Duct Syndrome, where parts of the internal female reproductive structures remain in a male with typical chromosomes and a typical phenotype. Males with PMDS cannot fulfill the female role because their phenotypes are organized around sperm, not eggs.

The case does not show male and female are unreliable. After all, this male produced sperm and fathered children! Rather, it shows us the importance of anti-Müllerian hormone in the disintegration of primordial female structures and the development of the male sex.[18] It shows us the various mechanisms at play in sex development, but it does not change or challenge male and female.

CELLS

After the genetics and hormone categories, Ainsworth moves to cells. Inside the cell's nucleus is your genome, the complete set of genes contained within chromosomes. Atypical cell composition within the body, such as having cells with a genetic makeup different from other cells in the body, can result in developmental disorders.

Differences in the genetic composition of cells, outside of the normal person whose diploid cells are all 46:XX or 46:XY, has led sex spectrum proponents to claim that cell variation shows male and female are unreliable categories. This is once again a conflation of two concepts: sex determination mechanisms and sex itself.

CASE 7
MOSAIC CELLS

Rarely, some people are born with a mix of genetically different cells in their body, caused by the development of a single fertilized egg with different genetic makeups. Some cells have a certain number or type of chromosomes, whereas others have another number or type of chromosomes. This is called mosaicism.[19]

And yet, using mosaicism to argue that sex is not binary is a category error. A patchwork of genetically different cells does not mean the person is not male or female. For example, if we recall from the beginning of the chapter, with the case study of the pregnant woman with a majority XY karyotype, we see that this woman has mosaicism: some of her cells are XX, and others are XY. Despite this, she did not develop as a male or "in between." She developed a large gamete phenotype, able to support ova, conceive, and give birth.

Having a unique set of chromosomes does not mean you will have a unique sex. Unusual karyotypes like mosaicism affect the body's physiology and how it may respond to disease, and so it's important to study the full range of possible differences within the sexes. But this does not mean rejecting they are reproductive roles with distinct phenotypes.

CASE 8
MICROCHIMERISM

Sometimes, the cells within a fetus can cross the structure that provides oxygen and nutrients to the baby during gestation (the placenta), and some of them can enter the mother's bloodstream (a phenomenon known as microchimerism).[20]

Fetal cells can be found in maternal tissues both during and after pregnancy, and these cells can potentially act as reparative stem cells, helping the body respond to tissue injury.[21] These cells have been found in women's bodies for as long as three decades. Microchimerism may in part be one of the many factors for why women, on average, live longer than men. It is not, however, as Ainsworth argues, evidence male and female are unreliable categories. She writes:

> This type of work has further blurred the sex divide, because it means that men often carry cells from their mothers, and women who have been pregnant with a male fetus can carry a smattering of its discarded cells.

There is one major problem with Ainsworth's statement: to think having a small minority of cells from another person's body in yours suddenly "blurs the sex divide" is to assume that for male and female to exist, they must be "pure" forms with no variation, nothing for them to share in common nor any diversity within the two. But this is an absurd conclusion. Male and female are distinct reproductive categories with distinct phenotypes. Atypical cells inside the body do not change this.

A man with a minority of cells from his mother does not suddenly become "intersex." A mother with a minority of cells from her fetus does not either. He's male because he developed the small gamete phenotype. She's female because she developed the large gamete phenotype. Neither of these microchimeric cases call into question what the male and female sexes are.

To say they do is to ironically reject the natural diversity within males and females and reinforce a strict, black and white binary that does not allow for variation within the two categories. In contrast, the true sex binary understands there are only two reproductive roles (male and female) with plenty of variation in anatomy and behavior.

CASE 9
DIFFERENCES IN XX AND XY CELLS

In the last case, Ainsworth discusses how sex difference research revealed cells with XX or XY behave differently independent from sex hormones. For example, a double dose of the X chromosome impacts the body's response to stress. She writes:

> The next challenge, says Arnold, is to uncover the mechanisms. His team is studying the handful of X-chromosome genes now known to be more active in females than in males.

Suddenly, Ainsworth is comfortable using the terms male and female as if they are definable categories, ignoring everything she has argued so far, including the very title of her piece, "Sex Redefined." Why? If she claims the sexes are blurry categories, then how do we know X-chromosome genes are more active in females? How do know what a female is in the first place? Basic contradictions like these are scattered throughout the sex spectrum argument but never addressed.

Whether it is Genetics, Hormones, or Cells, Claire Ainsworth argues that sex exists on a continuum, that congenital disorders prove male and female are unreliable categories, and that the complexity of sex determination mechanisms are proof of the sex spectrum. The problem, however, is that male and female have a universal biological meaning which applies both within humans and across a vast array of species.

This universal definition of male and female will not work for Ainsworth, however, because she does not view the sexes as evolved mechanisms. For her, each person can be reduced to singular traits along the spectrum: if you do not fit the platonic ideal of male and female (for example, that males must always have XY and females must always have XX), then you are not male or female. This idea, sex as a mix of traits detached from reproduction, is the foothold for the deconstruction of male and female by sex spectrum theorists and activists. Rare developmental disorders are used as the leverage to open the door. Ainsworth uses both strategies.

These strategies fail to validate the sex spectrum argument, however. Across genetics, hormones, and cells, we can clearly identify male and female by identifying the structures that support the production (gonads) and transportation (genitalia) of either gamete type. This is something Ainsworth never mentions, because she wants to conflate the diversity in people's bodies and the complexity of genetics with sex itself to make the categories of male and female seem undefinable.

While it is true the mechanisms involved in sex determination are complex, and that people's bodies can be wildly different in appearance, the result is simple and consistent: male or female. Rather than showing us the "idea of two sexes is simplistic," these rare cases show us that sex development can be simultaneously complex in its process and simple in its end result. In other words, there are many potential paths for developing as a male or female, but there are only two endpoints, thus reinforcing the binary system of sex.

As much as it may seem from the surface, Ainsworth's piece is not really about biology. It is about using biology as a tool to convince the reader of her own political conclusions: that male and female are social constructs, and that gender identity, an internal sense of self, is the most accurate marker of sex.

Ainsworth reveals this at the end of her piece, quoting a doctor who treats infants with DSDs:

> My feeling is since there is not one biological parameter that takes over every other parameter [social principle], at the end of the day, gender identity seems to be the most reasonable parameter [political principle].

"In other words," Ainsworth concludes, "if you want to know whether someone is male or female, it may be best just to ask."

It may be best just to ask? Is that really the most reasonable view of sex? That does not sound very scientific. But that is a feature, not a bug, in the sex spectrum argument, which requires obscuring sex for social and political purposes. In fact, Ainsworth's piece is not about redefining the sexes. If it was, she would have given a re-definition of sex. But she did not. Instead, Sex Redefined is about obfuscation and replacement: first, obscuring sex by overwhelming the reader with a vast array of scientific information irrelevant to the argument, and second, replacing sex with the completely unrelated political ideology of gender identity. *Sex Replaced* would have been a more appropriate title for her piece.

After the article was published, a Twitter user asked Claire Ainsworth, "In your piece, 'Sex Redefined,' are you making the claim there are more than two sexes?" Ainsworth then responded, "No, not at all. Two sexes, with a continuum of variation in anatomy / physiology."

It is clear Ainsworth knows what male and female are, not only from this comment but also from her own biology research, and yet she prioritizes the social and political efforts to redefine sex according to subjective identity over the reality of our sexed bodies.

SUMMARY

- Sexes are ancient. Male and female are fundamental properties of human beings, the 1.2-billion-year-old mechanisms by which we reproduce. And such mechanisms of evolution have created important sex differences across biological, psychological, and social levels.
- Sex development is complex, but sex is not. The genetic and hormonal mechanisms involved in sex development are multidimensional, and yet these systems result in males or females, not a new sexes nor someone between sexes.
- The sex of individuals is important. It is often very important to know whether someone is male or female, and other times, it does not matter. Just asking someone whether they are male or female is not the right approach in all situations. Scientific, medical, legal, and social contexts all require us to know someone's sex, sometimes for the person's own health and safety and sometimes for the health and safety of others.
- Sexes are not redefinable. There is no need to redefine the sexes of male and female to accept those who are atypical. In fact, those with sex development conditions and those who are trans can only exist because there are only two sexes, male and female. Thus, the irony becomes clear: Erasing male and female would mean erasing both such groups.

CHAPTER REFERENCES

1. Lehtonen, J., Parker, G. (2014). Gamete competition, gamete limitation, and the evolution of two sexes. *Molecular Human Reproduction, 20(12).*
2. Dumic, M., et al. (2008). Report of fertility in a woman with a predominantly 46,XY karyotype in a family with multiple disorders of sexual development. *The Journal of Clinical Endocrinology and Metabolism, 93(1),* 182-189.
3. Eggers, S., Sinclair, A. (2012). Mammalian sex determination: Insights from humans and mice. *Chromosome Res, 20.*
4. Kimball, J. (2020). Sex chromosomes. LibreText.org
5. Leon, N., Reyes, A., Harley, V. (2019). Differences of sex development: the road to diagnosis. *Lancet Diabetes Endocrinology, 7(7),* 1-15.
6. Kashimada, K., Koopman, P. (2010). Sry: the master switch in mammalian sex determination. *Development, 137.*
7. Kimball, J. (2020).
8. Eggers, S., Sinclair, A. (2012).
9. Warr, N., et al. (2012). The molecular and cellular basis of gonadal sex reversal in mice and humans. *WIREs Dev Bio, 1.*
10. Lanciotti, L., et al. (2019). Different clinical presentations and management in complete androgen insensitivity syndrome (CAIS). *International Journal of Environmental Research and Public Health, 16(7).*
11. Wang, S., et al. (2009). Androgen receptor roles in spermatogenesis and fertility: Lessons from testicular cell-specific androgen receptor knockout mice. *Endocrine Reviews, 30(2),* 119-132.
12. Oakes, M., et al. (2008). Complete androgen insensitivity syndrome: a review. *Journal of Pediatric and Adolescent Gynecology, 21(6).*
13. Barros, B., et al. (2021). Complete androgen insensitivity syndrome and risk of gonadal malignancy: a systematic review. *Annals of Pediatric Endocrinology & Metabolism, 26(1),* 19-23.
14. Bachelot, A., et al. (2017). Management of endocrine disease: CAH due to 21-hydroxylase deficiency: update on the management of adult patients and prenatal treatment. *European Journal of Endocrinology, 176(4).*

15. Colet-Ipulan, L. (2022). Sexual dimorphism through androgen signaling; from external genitalia to muscles. *Frontiers in Endocrinology, 13.*
16. Sherwani, A., et al. (2014). Hysterectomy in a male: A rare case report. *International Journal of Surgery Case Reports, 5.*
17. Chua, I., et al. (2022). Persistent Müllerian Duct Syndrome: understanding the challenges. *Case Reports in Urology, 2022,* 2643833.
18. Josso, N., et al. (2020). What does AMH tell us in pediatric disorders of sex development? *Frontiers in Endocrinology, 11.*
19. Thorpe, J., et al. (2020). Mosaicism in human health and disease. *Annual Reviews in Genetics, 23(54),* 487-510.
20. Shrivastava, S., et al. (2019). Microchimerism: a new concept. *Journal of Oral and Maxillofacial Pathology, 23(2).*
21. O'Donoghue, K. (2008). Fetal microchimerism and maternal health during and after pregnancy. *Obstetric Medicine, 2008, 1.*

ARGUMENT 7

"STOP USING PHONY SCIENCE TO JUSTIFY TRANSPHOBIA"

SCIENTIFIC AMERICAN

The Scientific American article "Stop Using Phony Science to Justify Transphobia" is another piece which uses the complex nature of sex development and the diversity of sex differences to argue that sex is not binary.

The author writes that three subjects help explain the transgender experience: *Genetics*, *Neurobiology*, and *Endocrinology*. Compared to the population, certain trans individuals may have unique differences in these three systems, and some might not. Let's explore whether these categories provide evidence for the sex spectrum.

GENETICS

"Nearly everyone in middle school biology learned that if you've got XX chromosomes, you're a female; if you've got XY, you're a male," writes D Sun, claiming this is a tired simplification. But even with the existence of other chromosomal combinations (karyotypes), this is not a tired simplification.

First, using atypical karyotypes (like X or XXY) in arguments to support trans identities is disingenuous. Why? Because trans people almost always have typical 46:XX or 46:XY karyotypes, and researchers have already asked and answered this question with scientific evidence.

In one study, conducted with over 300 trans individuals, 97.55% had typical karyotypes of XX or XY, matching their birth sex. Only 3 out of 368 had Klinefelter syndrome.[1] Such studies reveal using chromosomal anomalies to explain trans experience is ignorant at best or dishonest at worst.

Second, 99.98% of births are unambiguously male or female, the phenotypes that produce either sperm or eggs, respectively.[2] Even in cases of chromosomal anomalies like 45:X or 47:XXY, the fetus still develops into a female (in 45:X cases) or a male (in 47:XXY cases). The reason why chromosomal anomalies still produce a female or male is largely thanks to the activation of the SRY gene (usually found on the short arm of the Y chromosome). If the SRY gene is present and active, it initiates a complex set of gene cascades causing male development.[3] Fetuses with only one X that do not have the SRY gene develop as females, and fetuses with XXY that do have the SRY gene develop as males. This genetic system is so consistent that even in cases of XXX or XXXY, the fetus still develops as a female or male, respectively.[4]

The author then uses additional congenital disorders to argue against the sex binary: "XX individuals could present with male gonads. XY individuals can have ovaries." Those unfamiliar with sex development might be confused. How does this happen? Simple: the activation or inactivation of the SRY gene. For males with XX chromosomes, this occurs when the SRY gene moves onto an X chromosome, causing male development. For females with XY chromosomes, this occurs when the SRY gene is not activated, causing female development. Despite the author's claims that sex does not originate from chromosomal makeup alone, sex is indeed largely determined by the activation or inactivation of the SRY gene on the Y chromosome.[5]

Next, the author discusses how SRY activation initiates additional genes such as DMRT1, which maintain testicular tissue.[6] This is true. If these genes are not present during fetal development, the testes may not develop, and you will develop as a female. But again, you might ask, what do these congenital conditions of the reproductive tract (DSDs) have to do with trans individuals, who almost always develop with typical chromosomes and typical reproductive systems? The answer is because these DSDs are being used for ideological purposes.

NEUROBIOLOGY

Here, the author uses neuroscience in brain differences to argue that male and female cannot be clearly defined: "A half century of empirical research has repeatedly challenged the idea that brain biology is simply XY = male brain or XX = female brain." It is true that there are indeed no black and white "male" and "female" brains in the sense that brains of males all have the same traits and brains of females all have the same traits. There is plenty of variation in brain differences both within and between males and females. But this variation does not mean there is no clearly defined "male" or "female," because we define sex through the two evolved reproductive anatomies.[7]

Set aside the universal definition of sex for a moment and return to the brain. As it relates to sex differences in the brain, we can actually distinguish male from female. But if there are no black and white male and female brains, how can we do this? The answer is through combining the traits together in a multidimensional analysis. In fact, the average differences in the brain within and between males and females are large enough that when aggregated together, they allow us to predict someone's sex with up to 97% accuracy.[8] This is specifically done through analyzing the overall morphology of the cerebral cortex.

It is true trans individuals may have specific structures in the brain more typical of the opposite sex, but this is highly confounded by sexual orientation. Trans people who are homosexual tend to have brains which are more like non-trans homosexuals. And trans people who are heterosexual tend to have brains which are more similar to non-trans heterosexuals.[9] Thus, when sexual orientation is accounted for, differences in sexually dimorphic regions tend to be from sexual orientation, not due to trans identity.[10] Ultimately though, no matter the brain architecture someone has, differences or similarities do not change one's sex, since sex is defined by the reproductive system you develop and not your brain architecture. Atypical traits in the brain do not change your sex any more than other physical differences. Using brain similarities to argue that someone is the opposite sex is akin to using sex differences in height to argue that a short male who resides in the typical female height range is a female. Overlap in traits between two categories does not render such categories non-existent.

ENDOCRINOLOGY

After using genetics and neurobiology, the author uses hormone levels to "disprove" the sex binary: "But like all things biology, hormones cannot be limited to the pubescent idea of "estrogen = female and testosterone = male." Though this technically true, it does not capture the full truth. While males and females are both exposed to testosterone and estrogen, they serve different and important functions in the sexes.

For example, estrogen has an essential role in regulating the female's menstrual and ovulation cycles, whereas testosterone in males has an essential role in maintaining testicular tissue and producing sperm. Estrogen and testosterone do not exist in the same levels across the two sexes. These hormone levels, like differences in the brain, exist as normal distributions, an average for males and an average for females.[11] Placing the two normal distributions together on one axis produces a bimodal distribution, showing us how the two groups compare. For example, males tend to have 15 to 20 times more testosterone than the average female.[12] This serves important evolutionary purposes related to reproduction and sexual fitness. Such a difference is so large that the two distributions (T for males and T for females) almost never overlap.

But variance in hormones, even extreme variance, does not disprove the sex binary. For example, a male who has far less testosterone than the average male does not become "less male" or "more female." He's a male because he developed the small gamete phenotype.

CONCLUSION

You may notice a pattern in all three categories: (1) Genetics, (2) Neurobiology, and (3) Endocrinology. Differences in anatomy, physiology, and behavior do not mean sex is on a spectrum, but rather, that sex-related traits are on a spectrum within each sex. Sex differences within and between males and females exist as bimodal distributions, one distribution for males and one distribution for females. There is variation of hormone production, brain structure, and appearance, but this does not make a "sex spectrum." Rather, it makes a spectrum of certain anatomical and physiological traits.[13] The reason why we can place traits such as hormone levels on bimodal distributions is because of the sex binary.

The author is not wrong in presenting basic scientific facts about the variation of sex-related traits. Where they are wrong is arguing that because of differences in genes, neurobiology, and hormones, male and female cannot be reliably defined.

"The science is clear and conclusive: sex is not binary, transgender people are real," the author writes. The problem is that sex is binary. There are only two reproductive functions, and thus, two sexes. The existence of trans people does not disprove this model, and it does not invalidate them. Rather, trans individuals represent the differences in identity and expression found within the sex binary. We do not have to deny the fundamental reality of sex to understand their experiences. In fact, they could only identify with the opposite sex in the first place because male and female are real, biological categories.

The author tells us to stop using phony science to justify transphobia. But I have a different request: when will activists and authors of major publications stop using medical conditions such as DSDs in political arguments about an unrelated group? And finally, when will activists stop using the beautiful complexity and diversity of biology to justify the dismantling of male and female under the guise of "science"?

SUMMARY

- Arguing that sex is a spectrum due to atypical genetics, neurobiology, or hormonal variation conflates these three categories with sex itself. This is a category error.
- Sex is defined as the phenotypes that produce either sperm or eggs. Those with genetic disorders like XXY or whose chromosomes mismatch their body (like XX males or XY females) develop either the phenotype that produces sperm or the phenotype that produces eggs. Thus, they are either male or female. Trans individuals also develop either of these two phenotypes, and are thus, either male or female.
- It is true there is no single set of features in the brains of males or in the brains of females. There are plenty of similarities, and there are also plenty of differences, forming average distributions. Sex is not defined by one's brain, so it cannot be used to argue that sex is binary or a spectrum. And brain differences cannot be used to argue that trans people are the sex they claim to be.
- Hormonal differences do overlap between the sexes, but not by much. Testosterone has specific and unique roles for males just as estrogen has specific and unique roles for females. Male and female are not defined by hormone levels, but there are sex-specific levels and functions of certain hormones.
- Recognizing that sex is binary and immutable in humans does not deny anyone's experiences. Variation in genetics, neurobiology, and hormones does not prove a trans person is the sex they claim to be, nor does it prove sex is a spectrum.

CHAPTER REFERENCES

1. Inoubli, A., et al. (2011). Karyotyping: is it worthwhile in transsexualism? *The Journal of Sexual Medicine, 8(2).*
2. Sax, L. (2002). How common is intersex? A response to Anne Fausto-Sterling. *The Journal of Sex Research, 39(3).*
3. Gilbert, SF. (2000). *Chromosomal sex determination in mammals.* In: Developmental Biology, 6th edition. Sunderland (MA), Sinauer Associates.
4. Kimball, J. (2020). Sex chromosomes. *LibreText.org.*
5. Kashimada, K., Koopman, P. (2010). Sry: the master switch in mammalian sex determination. *Development, 137.*
6. Matson, C., et al. (2011). DMRT1 prevents female reprogramming in the postnatal mammalian testis. *Nature.*
7. Lehtonen, J., Parker, G. (2014). Gamete competition, gamete limitation, and the evolution of two sexes. *Molecular Human Reproduction, 20(12).*
8. Luo, Z., et al. (2019). Gender identification of human corticol 3-D morphology using hierarchical sparsity. *Frontiers in Human Neuroscience.*
9. Manzouri, A., Savic, I. (2019). Possible neurobiological underpinnings of homosexuality and gender dysphoria. *Cerebral Cortex, 29.*
10. Feusner, J., et al. (2017). Intrinsic network connectivity and own body perception in gender dysphoria. *Brain Imaging Behavior, 11(4).*
11. Ellis, L. (2011). Identifying and explaining apparent universal sex differences in cognition and behavior. *Personality and Individual Differences, 51.*
12. Handelsman, D., Hirschberg, A., Bermon, S. (2018). Circulating testosterone as the hormonal basis of sex differences in athletic performance. *Endocrine Reviews, 39(5), 803-829.*
13. Schmitt, D. (2016). Sex and gender are dials, not switches. *Psychology Today.*

ARGUMENT 8

"VISUALIZING SEX AS A SPECTRUM"

SCIENTIFIC AMERICAN

Many of us are visual learners. We learn through graphics, diagrams, and charts. Through visual means, complex topics can often be transformed into beautifully simple concepts. There's one problem, however: pseudoscience spreads well in this form. When falsehoods are wrapped in graphics that are appealing to the eye, they are easy to overlook if one is not thinking critically. Scientific American's graphic, *Beyond XX and XY*, is a prime example of this phenomenon, where a falsehood gains power through its visual appeal, not its actual content.

Created by a graphics designer, *Beyond XX and XY* takes eight unique disorders of sex development (DSDs), places them on a colorful "spectrum" between male and female, and shows the development path of each, from chromosomes, genes, hormones, and genitalia.[1] It claims that some humans are not male or female because sex determination is far more complex than XX or XY. Since it was created, it has been used by sex spectrum proponents across the culture to argue that the male and female binary does not exist. Its effectiveness lies in its colors and visual complexity. The average viewer glances at the chart and is overwhelmed by the amount of information. From the surface, it looks professional and scientific, but it is nothing more than an exercise in graphic design. Despite it "looking pretty," the graphic has major problems, both in simplicity and in accuracy. Here's why.

First, *simplicity*: the chart is cluttered and complex. There are a vast number of boxes and a maze-like combination of arrows throughout. For example, some arrows from the left side of the chart travel across the entire graphic to the right, only to swerve back to the left. Furthermore, elements on the chart seem to be arbitrarily placed. Why not move some elements to straighten the arrows and simplify the design? If you need to communicate the development path of each condition, why not order the elements in a straight, vertical line for each, instead of the weaving arrows? The sheer amount of information combined with the visual mess makes *Beyond XX and XY* beyond understanding. Only those educated in the disorders are likely to understand the sequence of the boxes.

Second, and most importantly: *accuracy*. The concepts the chart is attempting to communicate are fundamentally incorrect. Its inaccuracy does not lie in the contents of the boxes themselves, because these boxes communicate facts about each condition. Rather, the falsehoods are found in the placement of the disorders on the entire chart.

If the chart simply showed the development path of each condition, then that would be accurate. The problem, however, is what the chart is trying to tell us: *people with DSDs are not male or female; instead, they are "in between."* But how is this proven? While we see eight unique, complex disorders placed on a single spectrum between male and female, there is no apparent logic for their placement.

Placing a specific condition on the spectrum requires a rationale or judgment for where each disorder should go. But where should they go? This "spectrum" has no measurable units. If there are no units, what decides which condition is closer to the female side than the male side? Or the male side than the female side? How is it decided where Klinefelter Syndrome goes? What about Congenital Adrenal Hyperplasia? Or Androgen Insensitivity Syndrome? The answer to this is never explained. That is because there is no objective measurement to decide how individual DSDs are ordered. Each of the eight conditions are unique, and they each result in a male or female.

The authors had a predetermined idea of where the disorders should go and arranged them between "typical biological female" on the left and "typical biological male" on the right. In other words, they simply placed them how they felt like it. The result is absurdity.

For example, take Congenital Adrenal Hyperplasia (CAH). It is placed to the right of XX male syndrome. This means XX male syndrome is "more female" than CAH. Why is this absurd? Because it implies that XX males, who have testes and a penis,[2] are "more female" than women with CAH, who have ovaries, a uterus, vagina, vulva, and a slightly masculinized clitoris.[3] Why is someone with a male reproductive system closer to the "female" side of the spectrum than a person with a female reproductive system?

The absurdity continues with other disorders, like Klinefelter Syndrome (47:XXY), a chromosomal disorder in males that results in smaller testes, decreased testosterone, and sometimes gynecomastia (breast growth). Klinefelter's is placed closer to the "female end" than Persistent Müllerian Duct Syndrome (PMDS), a genetic disorder in males that causes a failure of the Müllerian structure to disintegrate, leaving internal reproductive anatomy typically seen in a female, such as a uterus.[4] Why is a person with a full male reproductive system (Klinefelter's) further to the "female end" of the spectrum than a male with a uterus (PMDS)? By sex spectrum logic, a male with a uterus should be placed closer to the female end than a male with zero female anatomy, even if this is scientifically wrong. The placement of both Congenital Adrenal Hyperplasia and XX male syndrome is enough evidence to show the ordering was arbitrary.

Beyond the placement of the disorders, the graphic has other fundamental issues found in its narrative explanations. In a single paragraph, it applies all four strategies of the sex spectrum's biological principle: *detach sex from reproductive role*, *use medical conditions as exceptions to male and female*, *conflate sex determination mechanisms with sex*, and *conflate sex characteristics with sex*. Montanez begins by saying: "Humans are socially conditioned to view sex and gender as binary attributes. From the moment we are born—or even before—we are definitively labeled 'boy' or 'girl.'"

The author claims the designation of infants as boy or girl is founded in social conditioning, not biology, ignoring the fact our species is gonochoric (individuals are either male or female) and anisogamous (we reproduce through males and females). This is the detachment of sex from reproduction, because she fails to define sex in relation to reproduction, and instead defines it as a socially conditioned, mix of traits, comprised of genetic and chemical factors. In reality, we are not socially conditioned to believe we are male or female. We just are male or female, regardless of people's beliefs. We each have the phenotype that produces small gametes (male) or the phenotype that produces large gametes (female), even those with congenital disorders. This does not mean one must follow rigid cultural ideas about how a male or female should express themselves. But we cannot detach sex itself from reproduction, as this is not a cultural construction.

What about the determination of biological sex? It is, as she says, "staggeringly complex." Here we see a conflation of sex determination mechanisms with sex: conflating the genetic and hormonal systems that determine and develop an individual's sex with sex itself. The entire graphic by Scientific American is an example of this conflation. In fact, it's in its name: Beyond XX and XY. The author believes that "sex is binary" is equivalent to saying "sex is XX or XY." But chromosomes are not sex; they hold the genetic instructions which determine the development of one's sex. "Sex is binary" means there are only two sexes, not that there are only two possible combinations of chromosomes.

Through its large number of overlapping arrows, the graphic shows the various genetic and hormonal systems that contribute to an individual's development, but in its presentation, it confuses these systems for the definition of sex. Those not educated on the biology of sex often mistake these various systems for what sex is. Yes, there are indeed an "intricate choreography of genetic and chemical factors that unfolds over time" but this choreography has a simple finale: male or female.

To confuse sex determination mechanisms with sex is like confusing the ingredients of a cake with the cake itself. Just because there are many ingredient options for making a cake does not mean cakes are undefinable. Likewise, just because there are many genetic and hormonal factors for making a male or female does not mean male and female are undefinable.

Congenital disorders like Turner Syndrome, XX Male Syndrome, Congenital Adrenal Hyperplasia, and others on the graphic all result in a male or female because they each result in a small gamete or large gamete phenotype. For example, women with Turner Syndrome are female because they develop the structures that produce large gametes and support the gestation of offspring. This includes ovaries for the production of eggs, Fallopian tubes for their release and transportation, and a uterus to support gestation. Thus, because we are using the universal definition of sex (female is the phenotype that produces large gametes), we can clearly define the sex of a person with Turner Syndrome, even though she does not have the typical 46:XX chromosomal arrangement for a female.

Despite its popular appeal from sex spectrum proponents and laypeople who were enamored by the colors and visual complexity, Beyond XX and XY did not escape criticism from scientists and others for its placement of congenital disorders on an undefinable spectrum "between" male and female. People with these disorders also spoke against it, saying the placement of their conditions as neither male nor female furthers stigma and encourages people to see them as "other."

Scientific American's Beyond XX and XY graphic tries to look scientific by looking complex, but a brief analysis of its content shows us that it is a graphic crafted in absurdity: there are no units on this spectrum, and no way to objectively place the conditions. The graphic considers clearly identifiable males "more female" than clearly identifiable females, and it utilizes an incredible number of overlapping arrows and inconsistent placement of boxes to feign complexity. But don't be fooled by its visual complexity. There's not much under the surface other than an ideological and illogical placement of rare developmental disorders along an immeasurable spectrum.

Beyond XX and XY is yet another product created by sex spectrum theorists and activists to destabilize people's understanding of the two sexes and replace them with gender identity—one's subjective sense of self—in most social, medical, and legal spheres.

SUMMARY

- Sex development disorders are qualitatively different. Each one has a unique cause and unique effects. There is no objective method to place them on a spectrum between male and female. Some affect males and some affect females.
- Why are conditions that result in unambiguous females closer to the male end than conditions that result in unambiguous males? This reveals the arbitrary placement of the conditions.
- The overlapping arrows is evidence that this is not a spectrum. If this is supposed to be a spectrum, where is the X-axis?
- This is an exercise in trying to make a pretty looking chart, but it fails on the scientific level because it does not provide an objective model for placing such conditions.

CHAPTER REFERENCES

1. Montanez, A. (2017). Visualizing sex as a spectrum. *Scientific American Blog.*
2. Mohamed, A., et al. (2022). A rare case of male infertility: XX male syndrome. *Endocrine Abstracts, 86.*
3. Pereira, N., et al. (2018). Reproductive function and fertility in women with Congenital Adrenal Hyperplasia. *EMJ Reproductive Health, 4(1), 101-107.*
4. Josso, N., Rey, R. (2020). What does AMH tell us in pediatric disorders of sex development? *Frontiers in Endocrinology, 11(619).*

ARGUMENT 9

"HOW SEXUALLY DIMORPHIC ARE WE?"

AMERICAN JOURNAL OF HUMAN BIOLOGY

In this 2000 paper led by biologist and gender studies professor Anne Fausto-Sterling, the authors argue that 1.7% of the human population does not fit the "Platonic ideal" of sexual dimorphism—the idea that for each sex there is a "single, universally correct developmental pathway and outcome." Since then, the paper has been used by sex spectrum theorists and activists to deconstruct the meaning of male and female and redefine sex according to one's personal identity.

The authors make three claims:

1. There is no standard template for human males and females.
2. 1.7% of the population deviates from the ideal of male or female.
3. Anyone who does not fit the ideal form of male or female is "intersex."

Like most sex spectrum arguments, the paper employs the first two strategies of the sex spectrum's biological principle: *detaching sex from reproduction* and *using disorders as exceptions to the re-definition of sex.* Let's explore how they do this and how to respond.

Constructing a definition of sex. Instead of defining the sexes by their reproductive role, the authors define male and female according to very specific criteria:

> [A male is] someone with an XY chromosomal composition, and testes located within the scrotal sac. The testes produce sperm which, via the vas deferens, may be transported to the urethra and ejaculated outside the body. Penis length at birth ranges from 2.5 to 4.5 cm; an idealized penis has a completely enclosed urethra which opens at the tip of the glans.

> [A female is] someone who has two X chromosomes, functional ovaries which ensure a feminizing puberty, oviducts connecting to a uterus, cervix, and vaginal canal, inner and outer vaginal lips, and a clitoris, which at birth ranges in size from 0.20 to 0.85 cm.

For the authors, any deviation from this specific list of criteria, the *Platonic ideal*, means the person is intersex. By constructing a narrow definition of male and female based on a checklist of anatomical and physiological traits, the authors argue that any stray in development is evidence against the reality of male and female. This provides the authors a basis for the claim that 1.728% of the human population is intersex, not male or female. There's one major problem, however: this definition for "intersex" is too broad. It includes people who are unambiguously male or female, rendering the term's use scientifically and clinically meaningless. In addition to this, "intersex" does not mean that the person is not male or female, but rather that physical markers for their sex are conflicting. We'll explore this below.

USING DEVELOPMENTAL DISORDERS AS EXCEPTIONS

After constructing their narrow definition of male and female, the authors list a variety of developmental disorders that deviate from this set of criteria, adding up to their statistic of 1.7%:

- Late Onset Congenital Adrenal Hyperplasia (LOCAH)
- Congenital Adrenal Hyperplasia (CAH)

- XXY (Klinefelter Syndrome)
- XO (Turner Syndrome)
- XYY (Jacob Syndrome)
- XXX (Triple X Syndrome)
- XXYY
- XX male syndrome
- Mayer-Rokitansky-Küster-Hauser Syndrome (MRKH)

Let's analyze the various developmental disorders used by the authors to see if it is reasonable for people with these conditions to be considered not male or female.

LATE ONSET CONGENITAL ADRENAL HYPERPLASIA

The first, and most common, is Late Onset Congenital Adrenal Hyperplasia. It alone comprises a whopping 88% of the 1.728% number, meaning that 1.5% of the population has LOCAH.[1] [2] So, what is LOCAH? And does it result in someone who is not male or female?

LOCAH is one of many sex development conditions which affect the adrenal glands and hormone production in both males and females. Adrenal glands are located on the top of the kidneys and produce hormones which regulate essential functions in the body. LOCAH occurs when genetic mutations cause the adrenal glands to produce excess sex hormones known as androgens.

This excess androgen is caused by deficiencies in enzymes involved in androgen production, most often the 21-hydroxylase enzyme. Partial lack of 21-hydroxylase enzyme, as seen in LOCAH, results in lower cortisol production and an excess production of adrenal androgen.[3] Cortisol is a steroid hormone involved in the body's response to stress. It also aids in the metabolism of fat, protein, and carbohydrates. Low cortisol can cause fatigue, dizziness, weight loss, muscle weakness, and mood changes. Adrenal androgen, on the other hand, is a steroid found in both males and females, but it plays a more important role in adult women. In females, unusually high levels of adrenal androgens can cause acne, changes in female body shape, decrease in breast size, and menstrual cycle disorders. In males, it can cause acne, increased growth, and infertility. Second, does LOCAH result in someone who is not male or female? According to the universal definition of sexes—phenotypes that produce two differently-sized gametes—people with LOCAH are unambiguous males or females. This means they develop complete male or female reproductive systems involved in the production of sperm or ova, respectively. Affected females still develop ovaries, Fallopian tubes, uterus, cervix, and vagina; they almost always produce mature ova, can become pregnant, and give birth.[4] And affected males still develop testes, internal sperm transport systems, and a penis; they almost always produce mature sperm and can impregnate.

Knowing these facts, why do the authors include LOCAH as "intersex"? Any person with atypical development deviates from the narrow definition is seen as not male or female, even with complete, unambiguous, and fertile reproductive systems. The question reasonable people should ask the authors is why should hormone disorder make someone not male or female? Because LOCAH does not result in any ambiguity to a person's sex, nor any infertility, let's remove it from the list. Now, the statistic already becomes 0.228%, instead of 1.728%.

CONGENITAL ADRENAL HYPERPLASIA

Next is the classic variant of LOCAH and more severe Congenital Adrenal Hyperplasia, which the authors call the "most common cause of intersexuality in XX females." Is this an example of being "between male and female"? Unlike the late onset version, classic CAH presents at birth, with near complete 21-hydroxylase enzyme deficiency. This results in low cortisol and high adrenal androgen production. The condition affects about 1 in 13,000 newborns—a rate of around 0.0077% of births.[5] Both males and females with CAH often experience excess androgens and severe salt loss in the body, affecting fluid levels and blood pressure. In females, while the ovaries, Fallopian tubes, uterus, cervix, and vagina fully develop, the excess androgen produced from the adrenal glands often masculinizes the vulva and clitoris, a region highly sensitive to androgen exposure. This can result in the growth of the clitoris, atrophy of the vagina, and sometimes a fusion of the labia. However, with no SRY activation and no anti-Müllerian hormone, the fetus still develops the phenotype that produces large gametes. Thus, fetuses with 46:XX CAH develop as unambiguous females.

Like LOCAH, both males and females with CAH develop fully formed reproductive systems corresponding to their sex and can often produce mature gametes.[6] [7] Readers should ask the authors why a hormone disorder makes someone "intersex," not male or female. Because CAH does not result in any ambiguity to a person's sex, let's also remove it from the list. Now, the statistic becomes 0.2203%.

HYPOSPADIAS

Next are a set of development disorders called hypospadias, where the urethra opens on the underside of the penis rather than the tip. It is the second most common genital birth defect in boys.[8] Hypospadias are included in the Fausto-Sterling's paper with a rate of 0.05% of births but are not added to the 1.7% statistic, even though they are referred to as "intersexual births." Of course, you can only have this condition if you develop a penis, and are therefore, male. Among many factors that can cause hypospadias, a common cause is due to disruptions in dihydrotestosterone production (DHT), an essential hormone for enlarging a male's penis and descending the testes into the scrotal sac.[9]

Boys with hypospadias develop as unambiguous males, since they have the phenotype that produces sperm. The reader should ask the authors why boys with an underdeveloped penis are "intersex."

KLINEFELTER SYNDROME

Some conditions result in a fetus with atypical sex chromosomes combinations. Klinefelter Syndrome is one of the most common, where there is an extra X chromosome in males: a karyotype of 47:XXY instead of the typical 46:XY. The extra X chromosome commonly results in smaller than average testes, low testosterone levels, infertility, breast development, and decreased muscle mass and bone density.[10] It affects about 1 in 500 to 1 in 1000 newborn boys—a rate of around 0.092% of births. Because males with Klinefelter Syndrome develop testes, a Wolffian structure, and a penis, and can even produce sperm, they are unambiguous males and should be removed from the list. With Klinefelter Syndrome removed, the statistic becomes 0.1283%. Readers should ask the authors why an extra X chromosome from a chromosomal disorder makes an unambiguous male "in between" sexes.

TURNER SYNDROME

Turner Syndrome is another sex chromosome condition, where a female fetus is missing the second X chromosome. The missing or altered X chromosome affects development before and after birth, most often leaving affected females with a loss of ovarian function and mild to serious physical differences.[11] Turner syndrome is one of the more common DSDs, affecting about 1 in 2500 newborn girls—a rate of around 0.0369% of births. Because females with Turner Syndrome develop Fallopian tubes, a uterus, cervix, vagina, and vulva, and no male sexual organs, they are unambiguously female and should be removed from the list. With Turner Syndrome removed, the statistic becomes 0.0914%. Thus, readers should ask the authors why a missing X chromosome from a chromosomal disorder makes an unambiguous female "in between" sexes.

NON-XX OR NON-XY (EXCEPT KLINEFELTER OR TURNER)

The authors include additional sex chromosome disorders other than Klinefelter and Turner Syndrome to argue that the categories of male and female are unreliable. They list XYY (Jacob's Syndrome), XXX (Triple X Syndrome), XXYY, and XX male syndrome. What phenotypes do these conditions result in? And what are their rates?

First, XYY results in an unambiguous male phenotype: the fetus develops testes, a Wolffian structure, and a penis, and they are fertile. The rate is 1 in 1000 newborn males.[12]

Second, XXX results in an unambiguous female phenotype: the fetus develops ovaries, Fallopian tubes, a uterus, cervix, vagina, and vulva, and they are most often fertile. The rate is 1 in 1000 newborn females.[13]

Third, XXYY results in an unambiguous male phenotype: the fetus develops testes, a Wolffian structure, and a penis, and they are fertile. The rate is 1 in 18,000 to 1 in 40,000 newborn males.[14]

Fourth, XX male syndrome also results in an unambiguous male phenotype due to the presence of the SRY gene, translocated from a Y chromosome during reproductive cell division in the father's sperm cells.[15] [16] The fetus develops testes, a Wolffian structure, and a penis. Unlike other male DSDs, they cannot produce mature sperm because they are missing the AZF region from the Y chromosome, required for sperm development.[17] The rate is 1 in 20,000 newborn males.[18]

Since XYY, XXX, XXYY, and XX male syndrome all result in unambiguous and often fertile males or females, why do the authors include them as examples of people who are "between sexes?" Considering all their rates together (using the author's numbers of 0.0639%), and removing them from the list, the statistic now becomes 0.0275%.

MAYER-ROKITANSKY-KÜSTER-HAUSER SYNDROME (MRKH)

MRKH is a sex development condition in females which causes parts of the vagina, cervix, and uterus to be underdeveloped or absent. Unlike Klinefelter and Turner Syndrome, which are chromosomal conditions, the chromosomes of females with MRKH are the typical 46:XX.[19] Females with MRKH develop as unambiguous females: development of ovaries, Fallopian tubes, with an underdeveloped uterus, cervix, or vagina. The rate is roughly 0.0169% of newborn females. Because it does not result in any sex ambiguity, let's also remove it from the list. The statistic now becomes 0.0106%, or 0.01%.

RATE OF BIRTHS THAT PRESENT AS AMBIGUOUS

When we take the authors' statistic of 1.728% and subtract out all the conditions that result in newborns who are clearly male or female, we arrive at 0.01%. This is far, far lower than the 1.728% of births the authors propose are "in between" sexes, more than 100 times lower!

But, what about the ambiguous births? Can we accurately identify their sex too? The term ambiguous does not mean the sex cannot be identified, or that the person is not male or female, but that there are conflicting physical markers which can make it more difficult to objectively ascertain the sex. This is a more scientific and clinical definition of the term intersex.

Even if there are a handful of cases that result in a fetus whose sex is very difficult or even impossible to objectively determine, this does not call into question the reality of male and female and the ubiquity of these categories in humans and all other anisogamous species in the plant and animal kingdoms. Developmental disorders do not form additional sexes nor are they exceptions to the sex binary. Their rare developmental trajectories have helped us better understand the genetic and hormonal mechanisms that develop males and females. They are therefore part of the binary.

Even if we grant the authors' premise that not every single human being can be easily classified as a male or female, 99.99% of the population can, and the sex of remaining individuals in the 0.01% can be determined through analysis of their development path: what their reproductive anatomy is, how that anatomy developed in the womb, and how the various genetic and hormonal mechanisms caused that development.[20]

Now that we know the details of the conditions used by the authors to prove the sex spectrum's biological principle (sex is a spectrum between male and female) and social principle (male and female are unreliable categories), we see that the "1.7% of the population is between sexes" claim to be false. We now know that the 1.7% statistic has two major problems.

First, it is clinically problematic, because it lumps together a vastly heterogeneous group of conditions with unique causes and effects. This makes it impossible to diagnose and treat the conditions accurately if they are all viewed as one homogeneous group. Second, the 1.7% statistic is scientifically incorrect, because as our analysis showed, 99.99% of the population is easily classified as male or female.

But what about the social implications? How does viewing nearly 2% of the population as neither male nor female translate into the social space? The authors claim that society has forced people with these conditions to conform to society's ideas about what male and female bodies "should" look like.

Viewing people's atypical bodies as "freakish" or trying to alter them through genital mutilation was common throughout history and continues today. These practices must come to an end. But the way to end discrimination is not to answer back with, "Yes, these people are between sexes." This reinforces the clinically problematic and scientifically incorrect claims and fails to understand the development paths of people with these conditions and how to treat them. It also constricts and narrows the categories of male and female while othering those who do not fit one's "Platonic ideal" definition as provided by the authors. Instead, the way to end discrimination and provide accurate analysis based in the biology of sex is to include those with developmental disorders into the male and female categories, no matter how atypical or rare.

The irony is that, in their attempt to recognize those with atypical bodies, Anne Fausto-Sterling and co-authors reinforce narrow boxes onto them by creating rigid definitions of what's accepted as male or female. As we have seen throughout the book, every sex spectrum argument ironically creates this unintended outcome: by upholding human-centric, scientifically incorrect definitions of male and female (the mix of traits detached from reproductive function), sex spectrum arguments further a rigid socially constructed definition. For example, the authors' criteria that a male must have a specific penis length and urethral opening at the tip to be considered male excludes boys whose penis is underdeveloped or whose urethra is on the underside of the shaft, both due to developmental disorders. According to the authors' logic, an underdeveloped penis would place him on the spectrum as "less male" than a typical male, even though the function of his phenotype is to produce and release sperm like all other males. The only way we can diagnose the boy as a having an underdeveloped penis is by first knowing his sex: male.

By constricting the categories of male and female while othering those who do not fit the narrow definition, Anne Fausto-Sterling and co-authors are helping increase the chances of genital mutilation and discrimination, reinforcing the rigid "binary" they claim to be against. After all, if a boy with an underdeveloped penis is viewed as less male, what's stopping doctors and parents from thinking that we can make him "more male" through surgery and hormones? Males are defined as male based on the phenotype that produces sperm, not based on their penis size.

Othering people with developmental disorders through narrow, socially constructed definitions of male and female is not the only problem with the authors' argument. They claim these developmental disorders are not disorders at all but rather natural and normal variations within human development: "The normative nature of medical science uses as an assumption, the proposition that for each sex there is a single, correct developmental pathway."

Here the authors conflate natural, normal, and healthy all in one. Something can be natural without it being healthy or normal, and something can be normal and healthy without it being natural. Let's disentangle this. Are the sex development disorders mentioned by the authors "natural"? Yes. They are in that these disorders occur in nature, detached from human intervention. Are they normal? Not really, if we define normal as in commonplace or average. In fact, they are very rare compared to the non-incidence in the general population. Are they healthy? Not really, since most of these conditions do not result in healthy effects for the people whose bodies and minds are affected by them. Babies with Congenital Adrenal Hyperplasia can sometimes die because their bodies are not retaining enough salt, 25-50% of women with Turner Syndrome have some form of cardiovascular defect, boys with hypospadias have trouble urinating properly, women with MRKH cannot gestate children, and all males with XX syndrome are infertile.

In fact, most of these disorders result in not only infertility, but a wide range of other anatomical and physiological health issues that will never go away, requiring medical treatment for their entire lives. In many cases, if they do not receive consistent and accurate medical treatment, many will experience even more lifelong complications at best and early death at worst. Effective medical treatment for these conditions does not exist to reinforce arbitrary social expectations. It exists to serve the patient's health.

By claiming these conditions are not abnormal or unhealthy, that they are just healthy variations of human experience, the authors imply something dangerous: that people with these conditions do not need medical treatment. It does not take much thought to understand how this can have dangerous results for patients.

Understanding that these conditions result in abnormal and unhealthy effects on the body does not mean the person experiencing these effects is abnormal or unhealthy. This would be conflating the disorder with the person. People are not disordered. But like most sex spectrum arguments, the authors fail to delineate between these important concepts and instead muddy their argument by claiming such conditions are normal "variations." They are not.

1.7% of the population is not "between sexes" as the authors claim. 99.99% of the population is easily classifiable as male (the phenotype that produces sperm) or female (the phenotype that produces eggs). Sex is not defined as a narrow and rigid mix of traits proposed by the authors. As developmental biologist Emma Hilton has noted, sex is not "pick and mix." It's a highly sequential, coordinated set of characteristics organized around one of two functions: the production of sperm or the production of eggs. This is how we can easily classify 99.99% of the population, even with rare sex development conditions. This binary system has existed for 1.2 billion years and will continue to exist long after the article by Anne Fausto-Sterling and associates is forgotten.

SUMMARY

- Being male or female is not about checking a list of traits. To conclude this, sex must be detached from function and development must be ignored. Being male or female is about developing an entire body system organized around the production of either sperm or eggs. Genes organize the gonadal tissue (where the gametes are produced), and the gonad organizes the internal and external genitalia (where gametes are transported).
- Fausto-Sterling's 1.7% number mostly includes males and females with no ambiguity to their sex. 1.5% of the population includes typical females with an overproduction of androgen later in life, and 0.2% of births mostly involve unambiguous males or females born with disorders of sex development.
- After calculating the % of births whose sex can be easily identified, the "true" number of births that are difficult to classify without additional screening is around 0.01%.

CHAPTER REFERENCES

1. Trapp, C., et al. (2013). Recommendations for treatment of nonclassic congenital adrenal hyperplasia (NCCAH): an update. *Steroids, 77(4),* 342-346.
2. Sax, L. (2002). How common is intersex? A response to Anne Fausto-Sterling. *The Journal of Sex Research, 39(3).*
3. Livadas, S., et al. (2019). Management of the female with non-classical congenital adrenal hyperplasia (NCCAH): a patient-oriented approach. *Frontiers in Endocrinology (Lausanne), 10(366).*
4. Bidet, M., et al. (2010). Fertility in women with nonclassical congenital adrenal hyperplasia due to 21-hydroxylase deficiency. *Journal of Clinical Endocrinology & Metabolism, 95(3),* 1182-90.
5. NIH. (2020). 21-hydroxylase deficiency. *Genetics Home Reference, National Library of Medicine.*
6. Reichman, D., et al. (2013). Fertility in patients with congenital adrenal hyperplasia. *Fertility and Sterility, 101(2),* P301-309.
7. King, T., et al. (2016). Experience in optimizing fertility outcomes in men with congenital adrenal hyperplasia due to 21-hydroxylase deficiency. *Clinical Endocrinology (Oxford), 84(6),* 830-836.
8. Keays, M., Dave, S. (2017). Current hypospadias management: diagnosis, surgical management, and long-term patient-centered outcomes. *Canadian Urological Association Journal, 11(1-2 Supp 1),* S48-S53.
9. Bouty, A., et al. (2015). The genetic and environmental factors underlying hypospadias. *Sex Development, 9(5),* 239-259.
10. NIH. (2020). Klinefelter Syndrome. *Genetics Home Reference, National Library of Medicine.*
11. NIH. (2020). Turner Syndrome. *Genetics Home Reference, National Library of Medicine.*
12. NIH. (2022). 47,XYY syndrome. *National Library of Medicine, Medline Plus.*
13. Otter, M., et al. (2010). Triple X syndrome: a review of the literature. *European Journal of Human Genetics, 18(3),* 265-271.

14. Tartaglia, N., et al. (2011). A new look at XXYY syndrome: medical and psychological features. *American Journal of Medical Genetics Part A, 146(A12),* 1509-1522.
15. Page, DC., et al. (1987). Exchange of terminal portions of X- and Y-chromosomal short arms in human XX males. *Nature, 328,* 437-440.
16. Sinclair, AH., et al. (1990). A gene from the human sex-determining region encodes protein with homology to a conserved DNA-binding motif. *Nature, 346,* 240-244.
17. Vorona, E., et al. (2007). Clinical, endocrinological, and epigenetic features of the 46,XX male syndrome, compared with 47,XXY Klinefelter patients. *Journal of Clinical Endocrinology & Metabolism, 92(9),* 3458-3465.
18. de la Chapelle, A. (1981). The etiology of maleness in XX men. *Human Genetics, 58,* 105-116.
19. NIH. (2020). Mayer-Rokitansky-Küster-Hauser syndrome. *Genetics Home Reference, National Library of Medicine.*
20. Leon, N., Reyes, A., Harley, V. (2019). Differences of sex development: the road to diagnosis. *Lancet Diabetes Endocrinology, 7(7),* 1-15.

ARGUMENT 10

"UNTANGLING THE GORDIAN KNOT OF HUMAN SEXUALITY"

GENDER AND THE GENOME

Throughout the book, we have seen that all the sex spectrum arguments share a common theme: *variation should not be forgotten.* And this is true. But variation in biology must be studied within a developmental and evolutionary framework for it to be understood correctly. Anyone interested in understanding variation must ask what the cause of the variation is and how it fits within evolved biological systems.

For example, homosexuality in humans and in other species is not evidence against male and female, but rather an example of evolved sexual behavior within males and females. To understand homosexuality, we must first understand what the sexes are, how they originated, and what their function is. Homosexuality cannot be understood outside of male and female. But sex spectrum theorists and activists ignore these questions and instead blindly claim that mere existence of variation outside the norm disproves established biology.

In our last sex spectrum article entitled "Untangling the Gordian Knot of Human Sexuality", author and physician Dr. Marianne Legato uses many different types of biological variation to claim that humans cannot be divided into clearly defined units of male and female. Her fundamental argument is that variation in anatomy, gender identity, and sexual behavior is evidence that male and female cannot be clearly defined. But like sex spectrum theorists before her, she fails to ask fundamental questions about variation. For example, what is the cause of the variation and how does it fit within developmental and evolutionary biology? And what are male and female? Not asking these questions leads to absurd conclusions, like sociology professor Robyn Ryle's claim that "male and female are unreliable categories" or that "there are not two kinds of distinguishable male and female bodies in the world."[1]

Like Ryle, the author of our last sex spectrum article writes, "…it is now evident that humans cannot be characterized as members of 1 of 2 clearly defined units: male or female."[2] Legato claims that our society has long defined the categories of male and female in three ways:

1. Seamless congruence of gonadal and genital anatomy.
2. The internal agreement with yourself as either male or female coinciding with that anatomy.
3. The sexual attraction to those with anatomy opposite of you.

Legato's definition is a non-universal and socially constructed definition of male and female, not a biological one. Why? If you recall from previous chapters, male and female are universally defined in biology as the phenotypes that produce two differently-sized gametes. Males develop the phenotypes that produce sperm; females develop the phenotypes that produce eggs. The reproductive anatomy we develop is therefore organized around either of these two roles. It does not matter whether someone has atypical gonadal or genital development, nor what subjective sense of self they have, nor what sexual behavior they choose to express. The sexes will always be defined by the organization of the reproductive anatomy around the production of sperm or eggs.

But in Legato's very rigid definition of the sexes as strict alignment with anatomy, gender identity, and sexual behavior, she constructs a non-universal definition, conflating the categories of male and female with anatomy, gender identity, and sexual behavior. She is pointing out variation within males and females without first defining the sexes. In a sense, she's putting the cart before the horse. Because she fails to explain how the three categories of variation exist within male and female, her conclusions quickly become absurd.

For example, she writes, "Traditionally and simplistically, we have categorized humans as either male or female: In fact, this rigid dyadic view does not allow for nor explain the whole spectrum of variations in gender identity, sexual differentiation, and patterns of sexual activity."

Here Legato reveals her thesis: the social principle of the sex spectrum—that because sex is a spectrum, male and female are rigid, socially constructed categories that do not explain the full range of human variation. But if we understand the fundamental meaning of the two sexes, something the physician fails to establish in the paper, we can also understand the variation that has evolved and developed within them. Using Legato's examples, let's review the variation within anatomy, gender identity, and behavior and show how such variation exists within the two sexes, not outside of them.

ANATOMY

For the first category, Legato claims that variation in anatomy and physiology proves that humans cannot be clearly divided into male or female. She uses chromosomal abnormalities, gonadal development, and genital development to argue her case. Chromosomal abnormalities result from an atypical distribution of chromosomes in the father's or mother's gametes, causing the fetus to develop with a chromosome constitution other than the typical 46:XX or 46:XY. Legato writes:

> Errors in sex chromosome pairing, that is, XO (Turner Syndrome), XXY (Klinefelter Syndrome), and so on, can and do occur with profoundly important and permanent phenotypic modification, not only on sexual features but on a whole spectrum of body systems and tissues.

Here Legato uses two strategies from the sex spectrum's biological principle: 1) conflate the mechanisms that determine sex with sex itself, and 2) conflate sex characteristics with sex. Humans, like almost all mammals, use an X-Y sex determination system, where the sex-determining region on the Y chromosome (and the chain reaction it causes) results in a male fetus.[3] Atypical combinations of 45:X and 47:XXY are errors in this system, but they still result in a female or male respectively. Fetuses with 45:X develop the large gamete phenotype.[4] And fetuses with 47:XXY develop the small gamete phenotype.[5] Thus, they are not examples of additional sexes nor are they "in between."

Legato's second claim is that these atypical chromosome combinations result in "important and permanent phenotypic modifications not only on sexual features but on a whole spectrum of body systems and tissues." It is true the phenotypes of these individuals are profoundly affected, but the effects on their phenotype should not be viewed as harmless biological variations. The impact on body systems and tissues causes severe and lifelong negative health effects.

For example, all females with 45:X are infertile, and many will experience potentially fatal heart defects, kidney complications, diabetes, thyroid problems, and weakened bone development.[6] For males with 47:XXY, they are also often infertile, and many experience osteoporosis, cardiovascular disease, autoimmune disorders, type 2 diabetes, and hypothyroidism.[7] Viewing their bodies as normal and healthy variations does not help treat their symptoms; it obscures and dismisses them. In addition, viewing them as additional sexes beyond male and female muddies their development path instead of elucidating it, and it obscures the knowledge required to treat their sex-specific infertility. The truth is we can only treat their conditions if we first know their sex.

Next, Legato uses the fascinating biology of gonadal development in humans and other mammals to argue that the line between male and female is "precarious" and "delicate." She writes:

> The balance between the agents that produce a male gonad and those that fashion a female gonad is

> multi-factorial, delicate, and precarious; it has been termed by many investigators as 'the battle of the sexes.' At least two opposing set of genes are involved in the signaling pathway: SOX9 and FGF9 promote testicular development; WNT4 and possibly RSPO1 foster that of the ovary.

The developmental biology research into sex development across the span of the last few decades has revealed a constant push and pull between the genes which develop the gonads into testes and the genes which develop them into ovaries. In other words, the signals for making a male versus a female are in an antagonistic relationship: male-making genes suppress female-making genes, and female-making genes suppress male-making genes.

Thus, the gonads, the gamete making factories, are maintained by the expression of sex-specific genes and the repression of opposite-sex specific genes. Legato seems to imply that this balance can be shifted in development and potentially later in life, causing a "sex change" to occur.[8] If this is the case, perhaps the line dividing male from female is arbitrary after all! But this conflates two things: the mechanisms that determine sex with the definition of sex.

It's true there is a complex network of genes controlling the fetus's development down the male or female path. And it's true the male-making and female-making genes experience a push and pull through the establishment of the fetus's gonads. But these mechanisms still result in a male or female. Furthermore, once the genetic and hormonal mechanisms build the gonads and genitals, there is no going back. Molecular and cellular biologists studying sex development in mice reiterate this:

> This mutual antagonism at the molecular level seems likely to reinforce, or canalize, the consequences of the initial sex-determining events. The fascinating phenomenon of ovotestis development aside, the newly formed gonad is strongly committed to one of

> two possible developmental outcomes, and nothing in-between. The existence of a bipotential gonadal primordium presumably increases the risk that divergent genetic programs, both of which are natural to that primordium, might attempt to 'execute' at the same time, with disastrous consequences. Thus, an antagonism that acts to minimize this possibility makes evolutionary 'sense.'[9]

As the biologists note, the genes involved in determining the sex development path are mutually antagonistic, likely evolved to stop the male and female pathways executing at the same time, which would lead to the infertility or death of the mammalian fetus. Nature is very much involved in making sure males and females are consistently produced! Thus, the line dividing male and female is not delicate or precarious but a robust system maintained by genetics.

Even if we remove the genes that help maintain testis or ovary differentiation, whether in development or throughout life, the gonad can regress, but they do not change into the opposite sex gonadal type. For example, when the gene DMRT1 is deleted in male mice after birth, the Sertoli cells in the testes are reprogrammed into granulosa-like cells that "express FOXL2 and other ovary-enriched genes."[10] But these cells are frozen in the first division phase, unable to differentiate further. Thus, for us to change the gonadal type of a mammal to that of the opposite sex, we would have to reverse development and return to when gonadal differentiation begins.

Lastly, even if we could produce an example in mammals where the gonad type fully changes to that of the opposite sex, the organism would still be one sex or the other. This would not destabilize the definition of male and female. Why? Because they would still be either male (the phenotype that produces sperm) or female (the phenotype that produces eggs). Sex change already happens in many species of fish, like clownfish, who change from male to female by changing their testes into ovaries.[11] Their sex is defined the same as it is in mammals.

But unlike mammals, this is an evolved reproductive strategy, not a disorder or science experiment.

Third, and finally, for the anatomy category, Legato uses infants born with atypical genitalia to argue that we cannot clearly divide humans into male or female. This is one of the classic strategies of the sex spectrum: conflate sex characteristics, like genitalia shape, breast shape, hip width, or hormone levels, with sex itself.

Let's first review how typical genital development works. Internal and external genital development is regulated by hormones following the differentiation of the gonads into testes or ovaries. In typical males, the testes release testosterone and anti-Müllerian hormone. Testosterone helps build the male's internal genitalia, after which the hormone is converted into dihydrotestosterone (DHT), and this helps build the external genitalia (enlarging the penis and descending the testes into the scrotum). Anti-Müllerian hormone disintegrates the primordial structures that would have become a female's internal genitalia. On the other hand, in typical females, the absence of testicular testosterone and anti-Müllerian hormone allows for the full development of the female's internal and external genitalia, and the absence of these hormones disintegrates the primordial structures that would have become a male's internal genitalia.[12]

In those with disorders, genetic and hormonal anomalies can cause atypical development of genital shape and function. This can result in genitalia that is underdeveloped or malformed. According to sex development researchers Fleming and Vilain (cited by Legato), genital anomalies can occur in about 1 in 100 births. But does this show the dividing line between male and female is arbitrary?

A common form of atypical genital development is hypospadias, where the urethra opens on the underside of the penis instead of the tip, causing difficulties with urination. This can result from being underexposed to DHT or errors in genes upstream of hormonal regulation.[13] Boys with hypospadias are male because they develop the phenotype that produces sperm. Another form of atypical genital development occurs from Congenital Adrenal Hyperplasia (CAH) in 46:XX females, where excess androgen production from the adrenal glands results in more masculinized external genitalia for a female.[14] This means that the inner and outer lips of the vulva might be fused together or the clitoris might be enlarged. But this does not mean the female fetus is the opposite sex or "in between" sexes. Girls with CAH still develop ovaries, Fallopian tubes, a uterus, cervix, vagina, and vulva and clitoris, all with the internal and external wiring of a female.[15] Therefore, they develop phenotypes that produce eggs. Instead of recognizing this disorder in the context of female development, Legato claims that girls with CAH have "male" genitalia:

> Chromosomal females with congenital adrenal hyperplasia are born with male genitalia.

But these girls are most certainly not born with male genitalia. They have no testes, no scrotal sac, no penis, no structures for the transport of sperm. In fact, most girls with CAH grow up to be fertile females who can produce mature eggs and gestate offspring.[16]

But to make her case that the line dividing male from female is arbitrary, Legato wants the reader to think these females are somehow born with penises and testes. We can only assume Legato is either ignorant of these conditions or is being disingenuous. An enlarged clitoris is not a penis. A fused vulva is not a scrotal sac.[17] It is true the external genitalia are sensitive to androgen exposure which can change their morphology, but exposure to androgens in a female with CAH will not result in male genitalia.

Legato would claim that both cases above, hypospadias and Congenital Adrenal Hyperplasia, destabilize male and female because their genitalia differs from the norm. But this conflates sex characteristics with sex. Legato wants us to believe atypical genitalia is evidence that the line dividing male and female is arbitrary. According to her logic, because of their atypical genitalia, boys with urethral openings on the underside of their penis are not males, and girls with fused vulvas and enlarged clitorises are not females. It is difficult to communicate just how scientifically incorrect this is.

Let's use a quick example for analogy. Consider the skull disorder craniosynostosis. Present at birth, this congenital deformity occurs when the fibrous joints between the bones of the skull close too soon.[18] While the brain continues to grow, the skull does not, resulting in a head with a misshapen appearance. Imagine excluding this human being from the species *Homo sapiens* because they have an atypical skull shape. You're ignoring their entire phenotype, their genetics, and their development, and you're also reducing their presence in a clear biological category down to one atypical trait.

This is the absurdity of what Legato is arguing for when it comes to sex: the exclusion of a human being from their sex because of atypical genital development. When we stop conflating "what bodies look like" with sex, just as we do not conflate "what bodies look like" with species, and instead observe the entire reproductive anatomy in reference to the biological definition of sex, we find scientific clarity: boys with hypospadias develop the phenotypes that produce sperm, and girls with CAH develop the phenotypes that produce eggs. They are males and females, respectively. They do not destabilize the dividing line between male and female, but rather show us the mechanisms that develop male and female genitalia.

Atypical development of one trait, like genitalia, does not call into question the reproductive system that person developed, nor does it call into question their sex. Understanding sex development as an evolved, sequential, and coordinated process with the ultimate end point of developing reproductive anatomy to produce either sperm or eggs is essential for understanding how these developmental disorders exist within the binary system of sex.

The second category used by Legato to argue that humans cannot be clearly divided into male or female is gender identity, one's sense of self as male, female, both, or neither. Legato uses gender identity to argue that being male or female can be contingent on the brain, not just your reproductive anatomy. She uses evidence of people whose gender identities do not align with their sex to claim that the line dividing male from female is unclear. But this is conflating one's sense of self with one's sex. The sex spectrum's political principle—gender identity is the ultimate determinant of one's sex—is the premise of this section.

To try and legitimize the subjective concept of gender identity, sex spectrum proponents like Legato have turned to neuroscience research which seems to show that people with gender dysphoria, and by extension, trans people, have brains which align more closely to the sex they identify as, rather than their birth sex. This has been used not just as evidence that trans people are who they say they are but as a metric of sex determination by some researchers who wish to push the sex spectrum's political principle.

For example, sex development researcher Eric Vilain, who argued that trans women should be in female sports and who said that "gender identity seems to be the most reasonable parameter [of sex]", claimed gender identity was the next field of sex determination.[19] Further, Claire Ainsworth, author of the sex spectrum article by Nature called *Sex Redefined*, argued that "if you want to know whether someone is male or female, it may be just best to ask," implying that gender identity, not biology, is the most important indicator of a person's sex.

Like Vilain and Ainsworth, Legato follows a similar train of thought, that gender identity is biologically determined and that this supersedes male and female as we have traditionally understood them: "It is now generally accepted that neither gender identity nor homosexuality can be reversed by postnatal environmental conditions and experiences; they are biologically determined during intrauterine life and are irreversible."

Homosexuality aside, the supposed biologically determined nature of gender identity is used as evidence that trans people are the sex they claim to be because of their brain structure. The traditional "brain sex" hypothesis is that, because the brain develops later than the genitals, the brain and genitalia may develop in opposite directions, whether due to expression of certain genes or exposure to atypical levels of sex hormones like androgen or estrogen.[20] The result would be, according to sex spectrum proponents, a "female" brain in a male body or vice versa, placing someone on the spectrum between male and female. This hypothesis, however, is no longer tenable in neuroscience.

Males and females have, on average, differences in the brain that vary by sex, even after controlling for height and weight.[21] These regions are called sexually dimorphic. Though they are relatively small to moderate differences, they do exist. Like all sex differences, some males can have some traits similar to typical females, and some females can have some traits more similar to males, such as a short male or a tall female. The same concept applies to sex differences in the brain. Some trans individuals have been shown to have sexually dimorphic regions more like the opposite sex, providing evidence for sex spectrum proponents that trans individuals are the sex they claim to be. However, these claims no longer hold up, because it has been repeatedly shown that when you account for sexual orientation, the differences disappear. In other words, the differences in sexually dimorphic brain regions found in some trans individuals are not due the person's trans identity, but rather due to the cohort's homosexuality.[22]

Of the studies that showed differences in sexually dimorphic regions of the brain in trans individuals, not only did most studies have zero homosexual controls, but most of the trans subjects were homosexual or mixed.[23] This confounds the results, because sexuality was not controlled for.[24] [25] [26] Some authors even noted this in their own studies, saying that because they did not account for sexual orientation, their results could be due to sexual orientation or gender identity.[27] However, of those that did control for sexual orientation, the differences in sexually dimorphic regions in the homosexual trans subjects aligned closely with those of the homosexual controls. And these differences did not show up in trans subjects who were heterosexual.[28] [29] For example, one study of heterosexual male-to-female transsexuals revealed their brains aligned more closely with that of heterosexual male controls, showing no signs of feminization.[30] Another showed the sex-atypical findings in trans individuals became sex-typical once sexual orientation was accounted for.[31] Controlling for sexual orientation seems to eliminate the relationship between atypical sexually dimorphic regions and being trans. Sexually dimorphic differences in some trans individuals, once thought to be evidence of the "opposite sex brain" hypothesis, seem to be evidence of the subject's homosexuality.

Thus, studying both homosexual and heterosexual transsexuals in comparison with homosexual and heterosexual controls reveals that sexually dimorphic brain differences are not due to trans identity. Trans individuals who are heterosexual tend to have brains which align with heterosexual controls, and trans individuals who are homosexual tend to have brains which align with homosexual controls. The authors of one study exploring brain network connectivity differences concluded:

> The present data do not support the hypothesis that sexual differentiation of the brain in individuals with [gender dysphoria] is in the opposite direction as their sex assigned at birth.[32]

Knowing that differences in sexually dimorphic regions of the brain seem unrelated to having gender dysphoria or having a trans identity, we are left with a question: Can any of the experiences of gender dysphoric trans people be explained through neuroscience? Tentatively, it seems like they can. Some areas of the brain that are non-sexually dimorphic do show differences that are unique to having gender dysphoria and being trans, such as the default mode network.[33] This extensive and interconnected group of brain structures is involved in the perception of self and the body.[34] Differences in these areas can be neurological markers for conditions involving self-body perception, such as eating disorders, body integrity disorders, and even gender dysphoria.[35] [36] One 2019 study by neuroscientists Manzouri and Savic showed that in both FtM and MtF transsexuals with gender dysphoria, the functional connections within the default mode network were less pronounced than in both male and female controls. And these differences persisted even after controlling for sexual orientation. In her piece, Legato even admits that neurobiological indicators for gender dysphoria and trans identity are more linked to self-referential networks. Quoting a neurobiologist who studies the brains of both trans and control subjects, she writes:

> Gender dysphoria is related to the cerebral networks mediating self-body perception which are formed early in development and finally become permanent.

It is unclear why Legato thinks that gender identity misalignment, believing one is the opposite sex, somehow makes the categories of male and female unreliable. We can only know whether someone's "gender identity" is misaligned if we first know what sex they are. Being able to clearly divide humans into males or females is an important prerequisite to treating and understanding males and females who experience gender dysphoria. It is absurd to use one's sense of self, whether congruent or incongruent, as a marker for one's sex, and further, to claim that incongruence itself is evidence of male and female being undefinable categories. The incongruence can only exist if the two sexes exist.

The third and final category Legato uses to claim that humans cannot be divided into clearly defined units of male or female is homosexuality (male-male or female-female sexual orientation). Throughout the section, she provides a review of the evidence for the biological basis of homosexuality, citing evidence from twin studies, genetic studies, brain imaging, and atypical hormone exposure. Though these potential causes of homosexuality are fascinating, they do nothing to show that male and female are somehow arbitrary categories. Unlike the concept of gender identity however, which is a subjective sense of self yet to be proven with biological evidence (not to be confused with gender dysphoria), sexuality has clear markers which go beyond self-report, not only with one's sexual behavior but physiological and neurological responses to sex-based erotic stimuli.[37] [38] Like the conflation of anatomy and gender identity with sex, Legato's conflation of atypical sexual behavior like homosexuality with sex results in even more absurd conclusions. Whether a person is heterosexual (opposite sex attracted), homosexual (same-sex attracted), or bisexual (both-sex attracted), human sexuality is inextricably tied to there being only two sexes. We can only define a person as straight, gay, lesbian, or bisexual by knowing two important things: 1) the person's sex, and 2) the sex of the people they are (or aren't) sexually attracted to. If humans did not come in male and female forms, there would be no basis for heterosexual, homosexual, or bisexual orientations.

Legato is correct that homosexuality is in large part determined by biology,[39] rather than purely sociological effects, but she is wrong to the point of absurdity to use homosexuality as evidence against the male-female binary. The more offensive implication with her reasoning is that males and females who are homosexual are not male or female at all. For if homosexuality proves that we cannot clearly divide humans into male or female forms, then those who are homosexual must not be clearly male or female. Bigots of the past and present have used these exact talking points, relegating homosexuals to third categories and viewing them as neither males nor females. Now it seems as though sex spectrum proponents are doing the same, just packaged under the guise of compassion to accept those who are different. But accepting those who are different does not mean excluding them from their sex.

Showcasing variation is an integral part of the sex spectrum's biological principle. Like sex spectrum proponents before her, Legato uses such variability as evidence that 1) male and female are unreliable categories and 2) one's subjective sense of self is the determinant of one's sex. She concludes, "...the view the world's population can be separated into a clearly defined dyadic unit of male and female is defunct." But this assumes that, to be considered male or female, one's anatomy, gender identity, and sexual behavior must all fit a specific mold. According to Legato, you must have no developmental disorder, you must identify with your sex, and you must be heterosexual.

If you do not fit this narrow view of male and female, then you are a natural variation outside of male and female which should not be, as Legato writes, "...rejected, condemned, and if possible, 'corrected', either psychologically or anatomically." It is true people who have atypical anatomy, identity, or sexual behavior should not be condemned or corrected. They should receive accurate medical treatment if they need it, but this does not mean "correcting" them.

However, in attempt to be so inclusive that the male and female categories are dismantled, Legato argues for a regressive position instead. Like all sex spectrum proponents before her, by conflating variation in anatomy, gender identity, and sexual behavior with sex, she is creating and reinforcing narrow boxes and excluding millions of people from their sex. In reality, if you have atypical anatomy, an incongruent sense of self, or atypical sexual behavior, you're not both or neither sexes. You are still defined as male or female by the phenotype you develop that produces either sperm or eggs, the universal biological definition of sex. Legato fails to mention this universal definition because she wishes to detach sex from reproductive function and conflate it with a mix of traits, identity, and expression. But we can only define any of these variations because we know what male and female are in the first place. Diversity of anatomy, gender identity, and sexual behavior ultimately relate back to the male-female sexual binary: the phenotype that produces sperm and the phenotype that produces eggs. Male and female must exist as stable, real, biological categories for any of this sex-based variety to exist.

Unlike the sex spectrum, biology has the correct answers to variation within the world of evolution and development. Anatomical disorders in the gonads or genitalia, for example, do not prove that male and female are undefinable categories, but instead reveal the genetic and hormonal mechanisms that develop individuals into males or females. People with such disorders, like females with Congenital Adrenal Hyperplasia or males with hypospadias, are defined as male or female by the reproductive anatomy they develop with respect to gamete type (the phenotypes that produce sperm or eggs). We know this from knowledge of evolutionary biology, which reveals how the sexes evolved, what the sexes are, and how they are universally defined across all anisogamous species. We then understand these disorders through knowledge of developmental biology, which describes how the sexes develop in individuals and the mechanisms which control this process. Thus, understanding evolution and development helps us untie Legato's "Gordian knot" of human sexuality in the correct way and in the correct context.

However, Legato's method of understanding diversity in anatomy, physiology, and behavior does not actually untie the knot. Instead, it tightens it. Here variation is not understood within an evolutionary and developmental framework, but instead as an amorphous spectrum without any anchor to evolved functions. By constricting the biological definition of male and female to someone who fits a very narrow mold, Legato enforces the most regressive, bigoted, and stereotyped views fundamentalists of the past only wished to have: that 1) if you do not have anatomy that appears typical for your sex, 2) if your sense of self does not align with your sex, or 3) if you're not heterosexual, then you are not male or female. Readers can understand why this is both scientifically absurd and morally problematic. Out of a desire to show compassion to those who have been discriminated against for being different, Legato upholds and celebrates difference, yet she forgets true compassion requires not only the acceptance of difference, but also the integration of it into established categories.

Discrimination is not eliminated, and true acceptance is not shown, by embracing the scientifically incorrect and morally problematic claims that people who differ from the norm are both or neither sexes. There are only two sexes, yes, and within these two sexes, there is wide diversity of anatomy, identity, and sexual behavior. Integrating difference, not excluding those from their sex, is the path towards true compassion, scientific accuracy, and effective medical treatment when it comes the biology of sex.

SUMMARY

- Humans can be clearly defined as male or female in more than 99.99% of births by direct observation of external genitalia, because external genitalia tightly correlates to sex. Sex is defined as the phenotype that produces sperm or eggs.
- Legato conflates variation in anatomy, gender identity, and sexual behavior with male and female. This sex-related variation in humans can only exist if male and female exist. Variation in these three categories reveals the diversity of sex differences within males and within females.
- We agree there is nothing wrong with variation. In biology, variation is the norm. For example, there is huge variation in body type within males and within females. Yet this also does not mean developmental disorders which cause life-altering and life-threatening defects should be left untreated.
- Accepting those who have sex-related differences does not mean relegating them to a third category. It means accepting diversity as a byproduct of the evolved binary system of sex.

CHAPTER REFERENCES

1. Ryle, R. (2015). *Questioning gender: A sociological exploration*, 4th ed. Sage Publications.
2. Legato, M. (2018). Untangling the gordian knot of human sexuality: What is the biological basis of variations in sexual phenotype? *Gender and the Genome, 2(3).*
3. Gilbert, SF. (2000). *Chromosomal sex determination in mammals.* Developmental Biology, 6th edition. Sunderland (MA), Sinauer Associates.
4. Cui, X, et al. (2018). A basic understanding of Turner syndrome: incidence, complications, diagnosis, and treatment. *Intractable & Rare Diseases Research, 7(4)*, 223-228.
5. Bonomi, M., et al. (2017). Klinefelter syndrome (KS): genetics, clinical phenotype, and hypogonadism. *Journal of Endocrinological Investigation, 40(2)*, 123-134.
6. Ramírez-Ibarra, M. & Martínez-de-Villarreal, LE. (2016). Clinical and genetic aspects of Turner's syndrome. *Medicina Universitaria, 18(70)*, 42-48.
7. Bonomi, M., et al. (2017).
8. There is a phenomenon known as sex reversal, where the fetus develops gonads opposite of what is expected from the chromosomes, such as XY females with ovaries or XX males with testes. This occurs during prenatal development thanks to the presence or absence of certain sex-determining genes. But this is not the same thing as "sex change." See: Weber, C. & Capel, B. (2018).
9. Warr, N., et al. (2012). The molecular and cellular basis of gonadal sex reversal in mice and humans. *WIREs Dev Bio, 1*, 561.
10. Ibid, 566.
11. Khoo, LM., et al. (2018). Growth pattern, diet, and reproductive biology of the clownfish Amphiprion ocellaris in waters of Pulau Tioman, Malaysia. *The Egyptian Journal of Aquatic Research, 44(3)*, 233-239..
12. Rey, R., Josso, N., Racine, C. (2020). Sexual differentiation. In: *Endotext.* South Dartmouth, MDText, Inc.
13. Bouty, A., et al. (2015). The genetic and environmental factors underlying hypospadias. *Sex Development, 9(5)*, 239-259.

14. Bachelot, A., et al. (2017). Management of endocrine disease: Congenital adrenal hyperplasia due to 21-hydroxylase deficiency: update on the management of adult patients and prenatal treatment. *European Journal of Endocrinology, 176(4).*
15. Pereira, N., et al. (2018). Reproductive function and fertility in women with Congenital Adrenal Hyperplasia. *EMJ Reproductive Health, 4(1),* 101-107.
16. Ibid.
17. Baskin, L., et al. (2019). Development of the human penis and clitoris. *Differentiation, 103,* 74-85.
18. Kajdic, N., et al. (2018). Craniosynostosis – recognition, clinical characteristics, and treatment. *Journal of the Association of Basic Medical Sciences, 18(2),* 110-116.
19. Ainsworth, C. (2015). Sex redefined: The idea of two sexes is overly simplistic. Nature, 518, 288-291.
20. Bao, A., Swaab, D. (2011). Sexual differentiation of the human brain, gender identity, sexual orientation, and neuropsychiatric disorders. *Frontiers in Neuroendocrinology, 32,* 214-226.
21. DeCasien, A., et al. (2022). Sex differences in the human brain: a roadmap for more careful analysis and interpretation of a biological reality. *Biology of Sex Differences, 13(43).*
22. Manzouri, A., Savic, I. (2019). Possible neurobiological underpinnings of homosexuality and gender dysphoria. *Cerebral Cortex, 29.*
23. Kurth, F., et al. (2022). Brain sex in transgender women is shifted towards gender identity. *Journal of Clinical Medicine, 11(6).*
24. Luders, E., et al. (2009). Regional gray matter variation in male-to-female transsexualism. *NeuroImage, 46(4),* 904-907.
25. Nawata, H., et al. (2010). Regional cerebral blood flow changes in female to male gender identity disorder. *Psychiatry and Clinical Neurosciences, 64.*
26. Uribe, C., et al. (2020). Brain network interactions in transgender individuals with gender incongruence. *NeuroImage, 211.*
27. Kranz, G., et al. (2012). Cerebral serotonin transporter asymmetry in females, males, and male-to-female transsexuals measured by PET in vivo. *Brain Struct Funct, 219(1).*

28. Manzouri, A., Savic, I. (2019).
29. Savic, I., Arver, S. (2011). Sex dimorphism of the brain in male-to-female transsexuals. *Cerebral Cortex, 21.*
30. Ibid.
31. Burke, S., et al. (2017). Structural connections in the brain in relation to gender identity and sexual orientation. *Scientific Reports, 7.*
32. Feusner, J., et al. (2017). Intrinsic network connectivity and own body perception in gender dysphoria. *Brain Imaging Behavior, 11(4).*
33. Khorashad, B., et al. (2021). Cross-sex hormone treatment and own-body perception: behavioral and brain connectivity profiles. *Scientific Reports, 11, 2799.*
34. Simon, R., Engström, M. (2015). The default mode network as a biomarker for monitoring the therapeutic effects of meditation. *Frontiers in Psychology, 6.*
35. McFadden, K., et al. (2014). Reduced salience and default mode network activity in women with anorexia nervosa. *Journal of Psychiatry & Neuroscience, 39(3),* 178-188.
36. Fang, A., et al. (2022). Maladaptive self-focused attention and default mode network connectivity: a transdiagnostic investigation across social anxiety and body dysmorphic disorders. *Social Cognitive and Affective Neuroscience, 17(7),* 645-654.
37. Arnow, B., et al. (2002). Brain activation and sexual arousal in healthy, heterosexual males. *Brain, 125(5),* 1014-1023.
38. Chivers, M., et al. (2010). Agreement of self-reported and genital measures of sexual arousal in men and women: A meta-analysis. *Archives of Sexual Behavior, 39(1),* 5-56.
39. Bogaert, A., Skorska, M. (2020). A short review of biological research on the development of sexual orientation. *Hormones and Behavior, 119.*

CONCLUSION

THE SEX BINARY

The new pseudoscience of sex has become dominant, from social media to science magazines and peer-reviewed journals. Never have so many institutions denied the systems required for us to reproduce as a species, the systems we embody every day. This lie portrays itself as "advanced biology," compelling others to believe in it with its misuse of knowledge and its appeals to moral righteousness, but its ultimate conclusion, that one's sense of self determines sex, cannot even be tested with the scientific method. It uses the veneer of science to claim it has the full story of sex, that we cannot reliably define male and female, but this is a facade with no structure.

What sex spectrum pseudoscientists call "advanced biology" is, in reality, the misuse and misinterpretation of biological knowledge for the goal of redefining sex. There is an irony in this strategy, however. In every biological paper they cite to claim the male-female binary is unreliable, such papers describe the observable facts of the two sexes, whether it is the mechanisms that produce male and female or the diversity of anatomical and behavioral sex differences across species. Because the two sexes are real systems in the world, as real as iron and gold, attempts at redefining them will always fail. Reality will always repudiate such false ideas. As famous theoretical physicist Richard Feynman once said:

> It does not matter how beautiful your theory is. It does not matter how smart you are. If it disagrees with experiment, it's wrong.

Biology—*real* biology—has a different story to tell, and this story is far more accurate than anything sex spectrum pseudoscience can provide. Biology shows us how the two sexes are universally defined across the plant and animal kingdoms. It tells us what the sexes are and how to recognize them, from the extraordinary feathers of the male peacock and the elegant ovules of a Ginkgo tree to the brood pouch of the male seahorse and the unusual reproductive system of the female hyena. It does not matter how different or similar the sexes look across species. Biology tells us that their sex is defined by their contribution of sperm or eggs to form a genetically unique individual.

Where fundamental biological facts provide us with the foundation for the two sexes, a true advanced biology reveals the vast diversity of genetic mechanisms that produce male and female within humans and across species. It explains how the sexes evolved and how they develop in individuals. It teaches us the details of how the male and female reproductive systems form and function, how the vast sex differences manifest within males and females, and how complex genetic networks consistently produce a simple outcome: males and females. Advanced biology also explores complex genetic disorders within the sexes and how they impact the lives of the people who have them, and it also provides such people avenues of life-saving treatment. The integration of basic biological principles with advanced insights provides us with a holistic picture for the biology of sex and sex differences. Sex spectrum pseudoscience cannot do any of this. It lacks predictive and explanatory power, basic scientific standards, and ultimately, truth.

If we wish to dismantle the false claims of the sex spectrum myth and slow its advance into our institutions, we must reject the lies that the male and female sexes are unreliable categories and that one's sense of self determines sex. We must refuse to participate in the *spectrum* belief system and stop supporting institutions who promulgate its lies.

Refusing participation is not enough, however. We must also spread a truthful and scientific vision for the future in its place. Doing so requires a return to our biological roots. We need to understand what the sexes are, where they originate, and how they impact us as individuals. Only then can we uphold a positive vision for the future where someone's sex is recognized as a critical variable in many aspects of life, where the important differences between males and females are explored with an open mind for each person's wellbeing, safety, and happiness.

While we explore and understand the importance of sex, we must also reject the idea that male and female are constraining categories. We need to accept ourselves as the males or females that we are, knowing that we can only be free when we accept the bodies we inhabit. Once we do, we can appreciate the beauty of our sexed bodies, the differences and similarities between us as males and females. Acceptance helps us appreciate the diversity of the sexes within our own species and the remarkable male and female variation across the plant and animal kingdoms. Perhaps some of those who have pushed the sex spectrum myth will also realize that accepting those who are different does not require a rejection of our biology, for it is our biology that gives us our uniqueness, embodied in the male-female binary.

No matter who tries to deny the ancient reality of the two sexes, we will always need words to describe the sex that produces the sperm and the sex that produces the egg, with all the profound differences that come from this fundamental distinction—the binary system of two.

BIBLIOGRAPHY

BOOK REFERENCES

- (2019). Legal enforcement guidance on discrimination on the basis of gender identity or expression. *NYC Commission on Human Rights.*
- Adrião, M., et al. (2020). 46:XX male disorder of sexual development. *Clinical Pediatric Endocrinology, 29(1),* 43-45.
- Ainsworth, C. (2015). Sex redefined: The idea of two sexes is overly simplistic. *Nature, 518, 288-291.*
- Anderson, M., Dixson, A., Dixson, A. (2006). Mammalian sperm and oviducts are sexually selected: evidence for co-evolution. *J Zool, 270,* 682–6.
- Arnow, B., et al. (2002). Brain activation and sexual arousal in healthy, heterosexual males. *Brain, 125(5),* 1014-1023.
- Atwood, M. (2020). Slug sex as an exception to male and female. *Twitter.*
- *Avise, J. (2011). Hermaphroditism: A primer on the biology, ecology, and the evolution of dual sexuality. Columbia University Press.*
- Bachelot, A., et al. (2017). Management of endocrine disease: Congenital adrenal hyperplasia due to 21-hydroxylase deficiency: update on the management of adult patients and prenatal treatment. *European Journal of Endocrinology, 176(4).*
- Bachtrog, D., Mank, J.E., Peichel, C.L., Kirkpatrick, M., Otto, S.P., Ashman, T.L., et al. (2014). Sex determination: Why so many ways of doing it? *PLoS Biol, 12(7).*

- Bao, A., Swaab, D. (2011). Sexual differentiation of the human brain, gender identity, sexual orientation, and neuropsychiatric disorders. *Frontiers in Neuroendocrinology, 32,* 214-226.
- Barros, B., et al. (2021). Complete androgen insensitivity syndrome and risk of gonadal malignancy: a systematic review. *Annals of Pediatric Endocrinology & Metabolism, 26(1), 19-23.*
- Bashamboo, A., et al. (2017). Anomalies in human sex determination provide unique insights into the complex genetic interactions of early gonad development. *Clinical Genetics, 91,* 143-156.
- Baskin, L., et al. (2019). Development of the human penis and clitoris. *Differentiation, 103,* 74-85.
- Bayraktar, Z. (2017). Potential autofertility in true hermaphrodites. *The Journal of Maternal-Fetal & Neonatal Medicine, 31(4): 542–547.*
- Bearelly, P., et al. (2019). Recent advances in managing and understanding Klinefelter Syndrome. *F1000Research, 8(F1000 Faculty Reviews), 112.*
- Beukeboom, L, Perrin, N. (2014). *The evolution of sex determination.* Oxford, UK: Oxford University Press.
- Biason-Lauber, A., et al. (2009). Ovaries and female phenotype in a girl with 46,XY karyotype and mutations in the CBX2 gene. *Am J Human Gen, 84,* 658-663.
- Bidet, M., et al. (2010). Fertility in women with nonclassical congenital adrenal hyperplasia due to 21-hydroxylase deficiency. *Journal of Clinical Endocrinology & Metabolism, 95(3), 1182-90.*
- Blackless, M., Charuvastra, A., Derryck, A., Fausto-Sterling, A., Lauzanne, K., Lee, E. (2000). How sexually dimorphic are we? Review and synthesis. *American Journal of Human Biology, 12.*
- Bogaert, A., Skorska, M. (2020). A short review of biological research on the development of sexual orientation. *Hormones and Behavior, 119.*
- Boghossian, P. (2019). 'Idea laundering' in academia. *Wall Street Journal.*

- Bonomi, M., et al. (2017). Klinefelter syndrome (KS): genetics, clinical phenotype, and hypogonadism. *Journal of Endocrinological Investigation, 40(2),* 123-134.
- Bouty, A., et al. (2015). The genetic and environmental factors underlying hypospadias. *Sex Development, 9(5),* 239-259.
- Bruce, V., et al. (1993). Sex discrimination: How do we tell the difference between male and female faces? *Perception, 22,* 131-152.
- Brush, S.G. (1978). Nettie M. Stevens and the discovery of sex determination by chromosomes. *Isis, 69(2), 163-172.*
- Burke, S., et al. (2017). Structural connections in the brain in relation to gender identity and sexual orientation. *Scientific Reports, 7.*
- Butler, J. (1993). *Bodies that matter: On the discursive limits of sex.* Routledge.
- Butler, J. (1999). *Gender Trouble.* Routledge.
- Carlson, A. (2016). Sex, biological functions, and social norms: a simple constructivist theory of sex. *Nordic Journal of Feminist and Gender Research, 24(1),* 18-29.
- Casas, L, Rey-Saborido, F., Ryu, T., et al. (2016). Sex change in clownfish: molecular insights from transcriptome analysis. *Scientific Reports, 6.*
- Charlesworth, B. (1994). The nature and origin of mating types. *Evolutionary Genetics in Current Biology, 4(8).*
- Charlesworth, D. (2002). *Plant sex determination and sex chromosomes. Heredity, 88,* 94-101.
- Chekroud, A., et al. (2016). Patterns in the human brain mosaic discriminate males from females. *PNAS Letter to Joel et al.*
- Chen, T., Tian, L., Wu, F., Xuan, X., Ma, G., Tang, R., Lu, J. (2019). Clinical and genetic analysis in males with 46,XX disorders of sex development: A reproductive centre experience of 144 cases. *Andrologia, 51(4).*

- Chivers, M., et al. (2010). Agreement of self-reported and genital measures of sexual arousal in men and women: A meta-analysis. *Archives of Sexual Behavior, 39(1),* 5-56.
- Chua, I., et al. (2022). Persistent Müllerian Duct Syndrome: understanding the challenges. *Case Reports in Urology, 2022, 2643833.*
- Clay, Z., Zuberbühler, K. (2012). Communication during sex among female bonobos: effects of dominance, solicitation, and audience. *Scientific Reports, 2.*
- Colet-Ipulan, L. (2022). Sexual dimorphism through androgen signaling; from external genitalia to muscles. *Frontiers in Endocrinology, 13.*
- Cooke, L. (2019). Everything you know about hyenas is wrong—these animals are fierce, social, and incredibly smart. *Ted Ideas.*
- Cornejo-Paramo, P., et al. (2020). Sex determination systems in reptiles are related to ambient temperature but not to the level of climatic fluctuation. *BMC Evolutionary Biology, 20(103).*
- Cui, X, et al. (2018). A basic understanding of Turner syndrome: incidence, complications, diagnosis, and treatment. *Intractable & Rare Diseases Research, 7(4),* 223-228.
- Cunha, G., et al. (2005). The ontogeny of the urogenital system of the spotted hyena. *Biology of Reproduction, 73, 554-564.*
- Czaran, T., Hoekstra. R. (2004). Evolution of sexual asymmetry. *BMC Evolutionary Biology, 4(34).*
- D Sun, Simon(e). (2019). Stop using phony science to justify transphobia. *Scientific American Blog.*
- da Silva, J. (2018). The evolution of sexes--a specific test of the disruptive selection theory. *Ecology and Evolution, 8,* 207-219.
- Davis, G., Preves, S. (2017). Intersex and the social construction of sex. *Contexts, 16(1).*
- de Jong, T., Shmida, A., Thuijsman, F. (2008). Sex allocation in plants and the evolution of monoecy. *Evolutionary Ecology Research, 10,* 1087-1109.

- de la Chapelle, A. (1981). The etiology of maleness in XX men. *Human Genetics, 58, 105-116.*
- de la Chapelle, A., Hastbacka, J., Korhonen, T., Maenpaa, J. (1990). The etiology of XX sex reversal. *Reproduction, Nutrition, Development, Suppl 1, 39s–49s.*
- DeCasien, A., et al. (2022). Sex differences in the human brain: a roadmap for more careful analysis and interpretation of a biological reality. *Biology of Sex Differences, 13(43)*
- Del Guidice M., Lippa R., Puts D., Bailey D., Bailey M., Schmitt D. (2016). Joel et al's method systematically fails to detect large, consistent sex differences. *PNAS, 113(14).*
- Del Guidice, M. (2009). On the real magnitude of psychological sex differences. *Evolutionary Psychology, 7(2),* 264-279.
- Del Guidice, M. (2019). Measuring sex differences and similarities. In: *Gender and sexuality development: Contemporary theory and research. Springer.*
- Del Guidice, M. (2021). Ideological bias in the Psychology of Sex and Gender. In: *Political Bias in Psychology: Nature, scope, and solutions.* Springer.
- Dreger, A., Chase, C., Sousa, A., et al. (2005). Changing the nomenclature-taxonomy for intersex: A scientific and clinical rationale. *Journal of Pediatric Endocrinology & Metabolism, 18,* 729-733.
- Dumic, M., et al. (2008). Report of fertility in a woman with a predominantly 46,XY karyotype in a family with multiple disorders of sexual development. *The Journal of Clinical Endocrinology and Metabolism, 93(1),* 182-189.
- Eggers, S., Sinclair, A. (2012). Mammalian sex determination: Insights from humans and mice. *Chromosome Res, 20.*
- Elliott, Z., Breheny, C. (2022). Biology of sex: detailed analysis of Forrest Valkai's Sex and Sensibility Video. *Paradox Institute, YouTube.*

- Ellis, L. (2011). Identifying and explaining apparent universal sex differences in cognition and behavior. *Personality and Individual Differences, 51.*
- Elsher, P. (n.d.). Gish gallop (logical fallacy): definition and examples. *Fallacy In Logic.*
- Epelman, M., et al. (2005). Anisogamy, expenditure of reproductive effort, and the optimality of having two sexes. *Operations Research, 53(3).*
- Fang, A., et al. (2022). Maladaptive self-focused attention and default mode network connectivity: a transdiagnostic investigation across social anxiety and body dysmorphic disorders. *Social Cognitive and Affective Neuroscience, 17(7), 645-654.*
- Fausto-Sterling, A. (1993). The five sexes. *The Sciences, 33(2),* 20-24.
- Fausto-Sterling, A. (2000). Sexing the body: Gender politics and the construction of sexuality. *Basic Books.*
- Fautin & Allen. (1992). Anemone fishes and their host sea anemones, a guide for aquarists and divers. *Western Australian Museum, Perth, p. 160.*
- Feusner, J., et al. (2017). Intrinsic network connectivity and own body perception in gender dysphoria. *Brain Imaging Behavior, 11(4).*
- Gardiner, J. (2016). The bigger, the better. *Nature Evolution, 533(476).*
- *Gilbert, SF. (2000). Chromosomal sex determination in mammals.* Developmental Biology, 6th edition. Sunderland (MA), Sinauer Associates.
- Glen, S. (2013). Bimodal distribution: What is it? *StatisticsHowTo. com.*
- González, E., Martínez-López, M., Morales-Garduza, M. et al. (2019). The sex-determination pattern in crocodilians: A systematic review of three decades of research. *J Anim Ecol, 88,* 1417-1427.
- Goymann, W., Brumm, H., Kappeler, P. (2022). Biological sex is binary, even though there is a rainbow of sex roles. *BioEssays, 45(2).*

- Green, H. (2019). There are more than two human sexes. *SciShow, YouTube.*
- Hamerton et al (1975). A cytogenetic survey of 14,069 newborn infants. I. Incidence of chromosome abnormalities. *Clinical Genetics, 8(4),* 223-243.
- Handelsman, D., Hirschberg, A., Bermon, S. (2018). Circulating testosterone as the hormonal basis of sex differences in athletic performance. *Endocrine Reviews, 39(5),* 803-829.
- Hanna, E., et al. (2019). The lived experience of Klinefelter Syndrome: a narrative review of the literature. *Frontiers in Endocrinology, 10(825).*
- Helm, R. (2019). Let's talk about sex. *Twitter.*
- Hill, A., Eisenberg, D. (2016). The long and short of it: new insights on sperm length help demystify the complexities of sexual selection. *Asian Journal of Andrology, 18(6)*: 902-903.
- Hilton, E. (2018). Response to ScienceVet's 'Sex Spectrum' thread. *Twitter.*
- Hilton, E. (2021). Crocodiles use temperature-dependent mechanisms of sex. *Twitter.*
- Hilton, E. (2021). Dissociation of sex characteristics as individual markers. *Twitter.*
- Hoekstra, R. (1990). The evolution of male-female dimorphism: older than sex. *Journal of Genetics, 69(1),* 11-15.
- Holub, A., Shackelford, T. (2021). Gonochorism. *Encyclopedia of Animal Cognition and Behavior. Springer.*
- Hörandl, E., Hadacek, F. (2020). Oxygen, life forms, and the evolution of sexes in multicellular eukaryotes. *Heredity, 125(1-14).*
- Houghton, M. (2023). The incredible milk-producing male bat. *Bat Conservation International.*
- Inoubli, A., et al. (2011). Karyotyping: is it worthwhile in transsexualism? *The Journal of Sexual Medicine, 8(2).*

- Ioannidis, J., et al. (2021). Primary sex determination in birds depends on DMRT1 dosage, but gonadal sex does not determine adult secondary sex characteristics. *PNAS, 118(10).*
- Iwasa, Y., Sasaki, A. (1987). Evolution of the number of sexes. *Evolution, 41(1), 49-65.*
- Jones, R., Lopez, K. (2014). Sexual differentiation. In: *Human Reproductive Biology, 4th edition. Elsevier.*
- Jones, T., et al. (2016). *Intersex, Stories and Statistics from Australia.* OpenBook Publishers. 33.
- Jordan, B., et al. (2001). Up-regulation of WNT-4 signaling and dosage-sensitive sex reversal in humans. *American Journal of Human Genetics, 68,* 1102-1109.
- Josso, N., et al. (2020). What does AMH tell us in pediatric disorders of sex development? *Frontiers in Endocrinology, 11.*
- Josso, N., Rey, R. (2020). What does AMH tell us in pediatric disorders of sex development? *Frontiers in Endocrinology, 11(619).*
- Kajdic, N., et al. (2018). Craniosynostosis – recognition, clinical characteristics, and treatment. *Journal of the Association of Basic Medical Sciences, 18(2),* 110-116.
- Kashimada, K., Koopman, P. (2010). Sry: the master switch in mammalian sex determination. *Development, 137.*
- Keays, M., Dave, S. (2017). Current hypospadias management: diagnosis, surgical management, and long-term patient-centered outcomes. *Canadian Urological Association Journal, 11(1-2 Supp 1), S48-S53.*
- Kennon, J. (2013). The 6 Most Common Biological Sexes in Humans. *Joshuakennon.com.*
- Kessler, S. (1990). The medical construction of gender: Case management in intersexed infants. *Signs: Journal of Women in Culture and Society, 16(1).*
- Khoo, LM., et al. (2018). Growth pattern, diet, and reproductive biology of the clownfish Amphiprion ocellaris in waters of Pulau Tioman, Malaysia. *The Egyptian Journal of Aquatic Research, 44(3).*

- Khorashad, B., et al. (2021). Cross-sex hormone treatment and own-body perception: behavioral and brain connectivity profiles. *Scientific Reports, 11, 2799.*
- Kimball, J. (2020). Sex chromosomes. *LibreText.org*
- King, T., et al. (2016). Experience in optimizing fertility outcomes in men with congenital adrenal hyperplasia due to 21-hydroxylase deficiency. *Clinical Endocrinology (Oxford), 84(6),* 830-836.
- Kirk, D. (2006). Oogamy: inventing the sexes. *Current Biology, 16(24).*
- Kocer, A., Reichmann, J., Best, D., Adams, I. (2009). Germ cell sex determination in mammals. *Molecular Human Reproduction, 15(4),* 205-213.
- Kodric-Brown, A., Brown, J. (1987). Anisogamy, sexual selection, and the evolution and maintenance of sex. *Evolutionary Ecology, 1, 95-105.*
- Kovacs, J., et al. (2001). Lessons from 30 years of clinical diagnosis and treatment of CAH. *Clinic Endocrinology.*
- Kranz, G., et al. (2012). Cerebral serotonin transporter asymmetry in females, males, and male-to-female transsexuals measured by PET in vivo. *Brain Struct Funct, 219(1).*
- Kumar et al. (2019). Anisogamy. *Encyclopedia of Animal Cognition and Behavior.*
- Kurth, F., et al. (2022). Brain sex in transgender women is shifted towards gender identity. *Journal of Clinical Medicine, 11(6).*
- Lanciotti, L., et al. (2019). Different clinical presentations and management in complete androgen insensitivity syndrome (CAIS). *International Journal of Environmental Research and Public Health, 16(7).*
- Legato, M. (2018). Untangling the gordian knot of human sexuality: What is the biological basis of variations in sexual phenotype? *Gender and the Genome, 2(3).*
- Lehtonen, J. (2017). Gamete size. *Encyclopedia of Evolutionary Psychological Science.*

- Lehtonen, J. (2021). The legacy of Parker, Baker, and Smith 1972: Gamete competition, the evolution of anisogamy, and model robustness. *Cells, 10(573).*
- Lehtonen, J., Kokko, H., Parker, GA. (2016). What do isogamous organisms teach us about sex and the two sexes? *PTBS, 371(1706),* 1-12.
- Lehtonen, J., Parker, G. (2014). Gamete competition, gamete limitation, and the evolution of two sexes. *Molecular Human Reproduction, 20(12).*
- Leon, N., Reyes, A., Harley, V. (2019). Differences of sex development: the road to diagnosis. *Lancet Diabetes Endocrinology, 7(7),* 1-15.
- Lessov-Schlaggar, C., et al. (2016). The fallacy of univariate solutions to complex systems problems. *Frontiers in Neuroscience, 10(267).*
- Lipinska et al. (2015). Sexual dimorphism and the evolution of sex-biased gene expression in the brown alga Ectocarpus. *Molecular Biology and Evolution, 32(6).*
- Livadas, S., et al. (2019). Management of the female with non-classical congenital adrenal hyperplasia (NCCAH): a patient-oriented approach. *Frontiers in Endocrinology (Lausanne), 10(366).*
- Luders, E., et al. (2009). Regional gray matter variation in male-to-female transsexualism. *NeuroImage, 46(4),* 904-907.
- Luo, Z., et al. (2019). Gender identification of human corticol 3-D morphology using hierarchical sparsity. *Frontiers in Human Neuroscience.*
- Maeda et al (1991). A cytogenetic survey of 14,835 consecutive liveborns. *The Japanese Journal of Genetics, 36(1), 117-129.*
- Manzouri, A., et al. (2017). Anatomical and functional findings in female-to-male transsexuals, testing a new hypothesis. *Cerebral Cortex, 27.*
- Manzouri, A., Savic, I. (2019). Possible neurobiological underpinnings of homosexuality and gender dysphoria. *Cerebral Cortex, 29.*

- Matson, C., et al. (2011). DMRT1 prevents female reprogramming in the postnatal mammalian testis. *Nature.*
- McClaren, A., et al. (1995). Germ cells and germ cell sex. *Phil Trans R Soc Lond B, 350,* 229-233.
- McDonough, M. (2022). How medicine's fixation on the sex binary harms intersex people. From: A Question of Sex, Episode 2. *Scientific American.*
- McFadden, K., et al. (2014). Reduced salience and default mode network activity in women with anorexia nervosa. *Journal of Psychiatry & Neuroscience, 39(3),* 178-188.
- McGregor, A., et al. (2017). Sex as a biological variable in emergency medicine research and clinical practice. *Western Journal of Emergency Medicine, 18(6).*
- Mnif, M. Kamoun, M., Kacem, F., et al. (2013). Reproductive outcomes of famle patients with congenital adrenal hyperplasia due to 21-hydroxylase deficiency. *Indian J Endocrinol Metab, 17(5),* 790-793.
- Mohamed, A., et al. (2022). A rare case of male infertility: XX male syndrome. *Endocrine Abstracts, 86.*
- Montanez, A. (2017). Visualizing sex as a spectrum. *Scientific American Blog.*
- Murray, D., Teare, S. (1993). Probability of a tossed coin landing on edge. *Physical Review E (Statistical Physics, Plasmas, Fluids, and Related Interdisciplinary Topics), Volume 48, Issue 4, 2547-2552.*
- Muyle, A., et al. (2021). Dioecy is associated with high genetic diversity and adaptation rates in the plant genus Silene. *Molecular Biology and Evolution, 38(3),* 805-818.
- Muyle, A., Marais, G. (2016). Mating systems in plants and genome evolution. *Encyclopedia of Evolutionary Biology, Academic Press, 480-492.*
- Nagahama, Y., et al. (2021). Sex determination, gonadal sex differentiation, and plasticity in vertebrate species. *Physiological Reviews, 101(3),* 1237-1308.

- Nawata, H., et al. (2010). Regional cerebral blood flow changes in female to male gender identity disorder. *Psychiatry and Clinical Neurosciences, 64.*
- Nielsen & Sillesen (1975). Incidence of chromosome aberrations among 11,148 newborn children. *Human Genetics, 30(1),* 1-12.
- NIH. (2019). Classic congenital adrenal hyperplasia due to 21-hydroxylase deficiency. *Genetic and Rare Diseases Information Center.*
- NIH. (2020). 21-hydroxylase deficiency. *MedlinePlus Genetics.*
- NIH. (2020). 46,XX testicular disorder of sex development. *MedlinePlus Genetics.*
- NIH. (2020). 47,XYY syndrome. *MedlinePlus Genetics.*
- NIH. (2020). Androgen insensitivity syndrome. *MedlinePlus Genetics.*
- NIH. (2020). Karyotype. *National Human Genome Research Institute.*
- NIH. (2020). Klinefelter syndrome. *National Library of Medicine.*
- NIH. (2020). Mayer-Rokitansky-Küster-Hauser syndrome. Genetics Home Reference, *National Library of Medicine.*
- NIH. (2020). Swyer syndrome. *MedlinePlus Genetics.*
- NIH. (2020). Triple X syndrome. *MedlinePlus Genetics.*
- NIH. (2020). Turner syndrome. *National Library of Medicine.*
- NIH. (2022). 47,XYY syndrome. *National Library of Medicine, Medline Plus.*
- Nistal, M., et al. (2019). Disorder of sex development, 46, XY pure gonadal dysgenesis. *Encyclopedia of Pathology, 1-3.*
- O'Donoghue, K. (2008). Fetal microchimerism and maternal health during and after pregnancy. *Obstetric Medicine, 2008, 1.*
- Oakes, M., et al. (2008). Complete androgen insensitivity syndrome: a review. *Journal of Pediatric and Adolescent Gynecology, 21(6).*

- Osaka, A., et al. (2020). SRY-positive 46,XX testicular disorder of sexual development with ledyig cell tumor. *American Journal of Men's Health, 14(5).*
- Otter, M., et al. (2010). Triple X syndrome: a review of the literature. *European Journal of Human Genetics, 18(3), 265-271.*
- Otto, S. (2008). Sexual reproduction and the evolution of sex. *Nature Education, 1(1).*
- Otto, S. (2009). The evolutionary enigma of sex. *The American Naturalist, 174(S1), 1-14.*
- Ottolenghi, C., et al. (2007). Loss of WNT4 and FOXL2 leads to female-to-male sex reversal extending to germ cells. *Human Molecular Genetics, 16(23),* 2795-804.
- Page, DC., et al. (1987). Exchange of terminal portions of X- and Y-chromosomal short arms in human XX males. *Nature, 328,* 437-440.
- Parker, GA. (2014). The sexual cascade and the rise of pre-ejaculatory sexual selection, sex roles, and sexual conflict. *CSH Persp Bio.*
- Parker, GA., Baker, RR., Smith, VG., et al. (1972). The origin and evolution of gamete dimorphism and the male-female phenomenon. *Journal of Theoretical Biology, 36, 529-553.*
- Pärssinen, V., et al. (2019). Male and female preferences for nest characteristics under paternal care. *Ecology and Evolution, 9(13),* 7780-7791.
- Peppe, D.J. & Deino, A. L. (2013). Dating rocks and fossils using geologic methods. *Nature Education Knowledge, 4(10).*
- Pereira, N., et al. (2018). Reproductive function and fertility in women with Congenital Adrenal Hyperplasia. *EMJ Reproductive Health, 4(1),* 101-107.
- Perrin, N. (2011). What uses are mating types? The developmental switch model. *Evolution, 66(4), 947-956.*

- Pla, S., Benvenuto, C., Capellini, I., et al. (2022). Switches, stability, and reversals in the evolutionary history of sexual systems in fish. *Nature Communications, 13.*
- Ramírez-Ibarra, M. & Martínez-de-Villarreal, LE. (2016). Clinical and genetic aspects of Turner's syndrome. *Medicina Universitaria, 18(70)*, 42-48.
- Reichman, D., et al. (2013). Fertility in patients with congenital adrenal hyperplasia. *Fertility and Sterility, 101(2), P301-309.*
- Rey, R., Josso, N., Racine, C. (2020). *Sexual differentiation.* In: Endotext. South Dartmouth, MDText, Inc.
- Rosenfield, K. (2018). Hermaphrodite. *Encyclopedia of Animal Cognition and Behavior.*
- Roser, M., et al. (2019). Human height. *Our World in Data.*
- Rubin, G. (1984). Thinking sex: notes for a radical theory of the politics of sexuality. In: *Pleasure and Danger: Exploring Female Sexuality.* Duke University Press.
- Rudge, D.W. (2006). The man who invented the chromosome. *Heredity, 97(136).*
- Ryle, R. (2015). *Questioning gender: A sociological exploration, 4th ed.* Sage Publications.
- Sakashita, A., et al. (2019). XY oocytes of sex-reversed females with a SRY mutation deviate from the normal developmental process beyond the mitotic stage. *Biology of Reproduction, 100(3)*, 697-710.
- Savic, I., Arver, S. (2011). Sex dimorphism of the brain in male-to-female transsexuals. *Cerebral Cortex, 21.*
- Sax, L. (2002). How common is intersex? A response to Anne Fausto-Sterling. *The Journal of Sex Research, 39(3).*
- Schärer, L. (2017). The varied ways of being male and female. *Molecular Reproduction & Development, 84.*
- Schärer, L., Janicke, T., Ramm, A. (2015). Sexual conflict in hermaphrodites. *Cold Spring Harb Perspect Biol, 7.*

- Schärer, L., Pen, I. (2013). Sex allocation and investment into pre- and post-copulatory traits in simultaneous hermaphrodites: the role of polyandry and local sperm competition. *Philosophical Transactions B, 368(1613).*
- Schärer, L., Rowe, L., Arnsqvist, Q. (2012). Anisogamy, chance, and the evolution of sex roles. *Trends in Ecology and Evolution, 27(5),* 260-264.
- Schmidt, M. (2018). A second X chromosome could explain why women live longer than men. *Discover Magazine.*
- Schmitt, D. (2016). Sex and gender are dials, not switches. *Psychology Today.*
- ScienceVet. (2018). Biological sex is a spectrum. *Twitter.*
- Sharp, A., et al. (2005). Variability of sexual phenotype in 46,XX(SRY+) patients: the influence of spreading X inactivation versus position effects. *Journal of Medical Genetics, 42,* 420-427.
- Sherwani, A., et al. (2014). Hysterectomy in a male: A rare case report. *International Journal of Surgery Case Reports, 5.*
- Shrivastava, S., et al. (2019). Microchimerism: a new concept. *Journal of Oral and Maxillofacial Pathology, 23(2).*
- Simon, R., Engström, M. (2015). The default mode network as a biomarker for monitoring the therapeutic effects of meditation. *Frontiers in Psychology, 6.*
- Sinclair, A. (2001). Eleven years of sexual discovery. *Genome Biology, 2(7).*
- Sinclair, AH., et al. (1990). A gene from the human sex-determining region encodes protein with homology to a conserved DNA-binding motif. *Nature, 346,* 240-244.
- Stolting, K. N., Wilson, A.B. (2007). Male pregnancy in seahorses and pipefish: beyond the mammalian model. *Bioessays, 29,* 884-896.
- Taplin, C., et al. (2009). Disorders of sexual differentiation: How do infants with complete androgen insensitivity syndrome present? In: *Endocrine Secrets (Fifth Edition).*

- Tartaglia, N., et al. (2011). A new look at XXYY syndrome: medical and psychological features. *American Journal of Medical Genetics Part A, 146(A12),* 1509-1522.
- Thorpe, J., et al. (2020). Mosaicism in human health and disease. *Annual Reviews in Genetics, 23(54), 487-510.*
- *Thresher, R. (1984). Reproduction in reef fishes. T.F.H. Publications, Inc., New Jersey.*
- Trapp, C., et al. (2013). Recommendations for treatment of nonclassic congenital adrenal hyperplasia (NCCAH): an update. *Steroids, 77(4),* 342-346.
- Uribe, C., et al. (2020). Brain network interactions in transgender individuals with gender incongruence. *NeuroImage, 211.*
- van Zoest, M., et al. (2019). Sex assignment and diagnostics in infants with ambiguous genitalia: a single-center retrospective study. *Sexual Development, 13(3).*
- Vorona, E., et al. (2007). Clinical, endocrinological, and epigenetic features of the 46,XX male syndrome, compared with 47,XXY Klinefelter patients. *Journal of Clinical Endocrinology & Metabolism,* 92(9), 3458-3465.
- Wang, S., et al. (2009). Androgen receptor roles in spermatogenesis and fertility: Lessons from testicular cell-specific androgen receptor knockout mice. *Endocrine Reviews, 30(2), 119-132.*
- Wang, Y., et al. (2021). Cortical gyrification in transgender individuals. *Cerebral Cortex, 31.*
- Warnke, G. (2001). Intersexuality and the categories of sex. *Hypatia, 16(3).*
- Warr, N., et al. (2012). The molecular and cellular basis of gonadal sex reversal in mice and humans. *WIREs Dev Bio, 1.*
- Weber, C. & Capel, B. (2018). Sex reversal. *Current Biology, 28(21),* R1234-R1236.
- Weisberg, Y., et al. (2011). Gender differences in personality across the ten aspects of the Big Five. *Frontiers in Psychology, 2(178).*

- Wilhelm, D., Palmer, S., Koopman, P. (2007). Sex determination and gonadal development in mammals. *Physiological Reviews, 87,* 1-28.
- Witchel, S. (2017). Congenital adrenal hyperplasia. *Journal of Pediatric and Adolescent Gynecology, 30(5),* 520-534.
- Witchel, S. (2018). Disorders of sex development. *Best Practice and Research in Clinical Obstetrics and Gynecology, 48.*
- Woodward, D., & Murray, J. (1993). On the effect of temperature-dependent sex determination on sex ratio and survivorship in crocodilians. *Proceedings: Biological Sciences, 252(1334),* 149-155.
- Wright, C. (2020). Sex chromosome variants are not their own unique sexes. *Colin Wright: Reality's Last Stand, Substack.*
- Zhang, H., et al. (2018). The roles of the kisspeptin system in the reproductive physiology of the lined seahorse (Hippocampus erectus), an ovoviviparous fish with male pregnancy. *Frontiers in Neuroscience, 12.*
- Zimman, L. (2014). The discursive construction of sex. In: *Queer excursions: Theorizing binaries in language, gender, and sexuality.* Oxford University.

GLOSSARY

BIOLOGY OF SEX TERMINOLOGY

ANISOGAMY	A form of sexual reproduction involving the fusion of two differently-sized gametes (eggs and sperm). Originating more than one billion years ago, anisogamy is nearly ubiquitous across complex species.
AUTOSOMAL	Any chromosome that is not a sex chromosome. Humans have 23 pairs of chromosomes. 22 pairs are the autosomes. The 23rd pair is the sex chromosomes, X and Y. Most genes required for developing as a male or female are found on the autosomes, not the sex chromosomes.
BIMODAL DISTRIBUTION	A range of data with two modes (or peaks). The peaks indicate the most common numbers in a data set. Bimodal distributions usually indicate that there are two groups different being compared. Traits that vary by sex, such as weight or hormone levels, often form such distributions: one normal distribution for males and one for females.

BIPOTENTIAL GONAD	In early embryonic development, the gonad is undifferentiated and will develop into a testis or an ovary in a process called sex determination. All mammalian fetuses begin undifferentiated before mechanisms trigger the differentiation of the gonad.
CERVIX	A muscular organ in the female reproductive system that connects the uterus and vagina and plays a critical role in regulating the passing of fluids.
CHROMOSOMES	A threadlike structure of nucleic acids and protein found in the nucleus of most living cells, carrying genetic information in the form of genes.
CLITORIS	A female erogenous organ capable of erection and sexual stimulation. It plays an essential role in female sexual pleasure and develops from the genital tubercle.
DIOECY	A sexual system in plants where individual plants are either male or female (i.e. an individual plant produces either male or female gametes).
DISORDERS OF SEX DEVELOPMENT	A group of more than forty congenital medical conditions which can cause atypical development of chromosomes, gonads, internal and external genitalia in utero. Each condition is discrete and unique. Most result in unambiguous males or females. Some affect males, some affect females, and some affect both sexes.

EPIDIDYMIS	A duct structure that is part of the male internal genitalia, located behind the testis and used for the transportation of sperm into the vas deferens.
ESTROGEN	A steroid hormone that maintains the female reproductive system and the ovarian and menstrual cycles. Its roles, however, go beyond the reproductive system and impact cognitive health, bone health, mood, and more. Both males and females make estrogen, but females make far more.
FEMALE	The phenotype that produces the larger gametes (eggs) in anisogamous systems.
GAMETE	In anisogamous systems, a male or female germ cell with a single set of unpaired chromosomes able to unite with another of the opposite sex to form a new zygote. The form and function of the two gamete types, sperm and egg, is the universal difference between the two sexes.
GENES	Segments of DNA, the basic unit of heredity, transferred from parent to offspring. Some genes code for proteins to produce specific functions and characteristics, but many act as regulators of gene activity within cells. Genes are held within chromosomes.

GENETIC SEX DETERMINATION	A common mechanism for developing embryos into males or females where specific genes within the chromosomes trigger differentiation of the bipotential gonad into a testis or an ovary, determining the sex of the embryo.
GENITALIA	The reproductive organs of an organism primarily involved in the release, transportation, or reception of gametes. In males, the genitalia involve the epididymis, vas deferens, penis, and scrotum. In females, the genitalia involve the Fallopian tubes, uterus, cervix, vagina, and vulva.
GENOTYPE	The complete set of an organism's genes. Genotype often directly determines phenotype but can also interact with the environment to influence observable characteristics.
GONAD	The primary sexual organ, the factory for sperm or eggs. The gonad is an organizer, fashioning primordial germ cells into sperm or eggs and regulating the establishment of the internal and external genitalia through hormone production.
GONOCHORISM	Sexual systems in which the male and female sexes exist in separate individuals, i.e. a single individual is either male or female through their entire life cycle.
HERMAPHRODITISM	Sexual systems where the male and female sexes exist in the same individual. A single individual produces both sperm and eggs, either simultaneously or sequentially.

ISOGAMY	A more ancient form of sexual reproduction involving the fusion of similar-sized gametes. There are no sperm or eggs, and thus, no males or females in such systems. Instead of sexes, isogamy uses mating types: gamete genotypes that regulate compatibility between fusing gametes (often designated + or -).
LABIA	The inner and outer folds of the vulva, the external genitalia of the female reproductive system. They play an essential role in protecting the vagina and urethral openings from infection and contribute to lubrication and stimulation.
MALE	The phenotype that produces the smaller gametes (sperm) in anisogamous systems.
MEIOSIS	A special type of cell division in sexually reproducing organisms that reduces the number of chromosomes to form germ cells (sperm or eggs).
MITOSIS	A type of cell division that results in two identical daughter cells with the same number and kind of chromosomes, essential for ordinary tissue growth.
MONOECY	A sexual system in seed plants where separate male and female flowers are present on the same plant. Two sexes on one plant

MOSAICISM	A genetic condition where a person has two or more genetically different sets of cells in his or her body due to errors in cell division. It can affect blood cells, skin cells, and germ cells, and its effects can vary from mild to serious medical disorders.
MICROCHIMERISM	The presence of cells from one individual in another genetically distinct individual. The most common cause is pregnancy, where fetal cells cross the placenta and enter the mother's bloodstream. Fetal microchimeric cells can replace injured cells in the mother and promote healing after birth.
MÜLLERIAN DUCTS	The primordial structure that develops into the female reproductive system (Fallopian tubes, uterus, cervix, and upper vagina). The Müllerian duct develops in the absence of testicular testosterone and anti-Müllerian hormone and regresses in males.
OVUM (EGG)	A mature female gamete which must be fertilized by the male gamete. It holds most or all of the cellular resources for the developing zygote. Because of this, the ovum is much larger in volume than the male gamete and often moves much slower or not at all. It is usually produced in much smaller numbers because of its resource-intensive material.

OVARY	The female gonad responsible for the production and nursing of female germ cells into mature eggs, or ova. It plays an essential role in the cyclical reproductive system of females, from the growth of eggs and the preparation of the uterus for an embryo to the process of menstruation.
OVIDUCTS (FALLOPIAN TUBES)	Part of the internal genitalia of the female reproductive system essential for transporting eggs from the ovaries to the uterus. Eggs are most often fertilized inside the Fallopian tubes.
OVULATION	The phase of the menstrual cycle that involves the release of an egg (ovum) from one of the ovaries. It occurs roughly halfway through one cycle.
OVULE	A part inside the ovary of a plant that contains the egg cell and which develops into a seed when that cell is fertilized by sperm cells produced from pollen.
PENIS	The external male genital organ for higher vertebrates, necessary for transferring sperm to the female during sex.
PHENOTYPE	The set of observable characteristics of an organism, determined by its genotype and the interaction of that genotype with the environment. Sex is an evolved phenotype defined by the set of structures involved in the production and release of either gamete type. This is determined by genotype.

PISTIL	The female reproductive structure of the flower that consists of the stigma (responsible for receiving the pollen), the style (responsible for transporting the compatible pollen to the ovule), and the pistil (responsible for protecting the ovule inside where the egg resides).
POLLEN	Microorganisms produced by a male flower's anther. Pollen is not the same thing as sperm. Pollen consists of the gametophytes that produce sperm cells. When pollen lands on the female part of the flower, long tubes grow and shoot the sperm cells into the female's ovule, where the egg is housed.
PROGESTERONE	An essential hormone released by the corpus luteum in the ovary during the female reproductive cycle that prepares the lining of the uterus for a fertilized egg.
SEMINAL VESICLE	An organ in the male internal genital tract essential for fertility that secretes important substances for sperm motility and stability. Its substances help suppress the immune system in the female reproductive tract to be receptive to sperm.
SEQUENTIAL HERMAPHRODITISM	Sexual systems in which the male and female sexes exist in the same individual at separate times, i.e. a single individual produces sperm at some stages of life and eggs at another stage.

SEX ALLOCATION	The optimal allocation of male and female sexes to organisms, whether they are composed in the same individual or in separate individuals, and whether the proportion of males versus females is higher, lower, or equal. The exact form of this allocation depends on the species and its environment.
SEX BINARY	The biological fact that there are only two sexes, defined as the phenotypes that produce either sperm or eggs. Across species, the sex binary can be composed in the same individual organism (hermaphroditism) or in separate individuals (gonochorism).
SEX CHANGE	An evolved species-wide sexual strategy where, depending upon environmental circumstances, an organism may switch from producing one gamete type (such as sperm) to producing the other (such as eggs) to fulfill the opposite sex role for optimal sex allocation. Mammals cannot change sex.
SEX CHROMOSOMES	A chromosome involved in determining the sex of an individual organism. Mammals use the X-Y system, whereas birds use the Z-W system.
SEX DETERMINATION	The process by which genetic or environmental mechanisms trigger differentiation of the bipotential gonad into a testis or an ovary, starting the process of male or female development.

SEX DEVELOPMENT	The sequential embryonic process of determining and differentiating the sex of an individual organism. Sex development involves two major components: sex determination and sex differentiation.
SEX DIFFERENTIATION	Once the gonad has been established through sex determination, sex differentiation involves the divergence of the undifferentiated reproductive ducts into male or female internal and external genitalia.
SEX REVERSAL	A genetic error where the sexual trajectory of the gonad is changed to the opposite sex pathway before it has been differentiated, resulting in a sexual phenotype opposite of what is expected from the embryo's chromosomes. XX males are an example, where SRY translocation onto an X chromosome results in a male fetus.
SEX SPECTRUM	The sociological construct that sex exists on a continuum between male and female, that there is no reliable criteria for consistently defining the sexes, and that gender identity is the ultimate determinant of sex.
SEXES	Evolved reproductive strategies that produce two differently-sized gametes (one strategy is called "male" and the other is called "female"). They can be composed in a variety of ways across species (gonochorism, hermaphroditism, etc).

SEXUAL REPRODUCTION	The mixing of genomes via meiosis and the fusion of gametes to form a genetically unique individual. Sexual reproduction originated around two billion years ago with single-celled eukaryotic organisms. Now, more than 99.9% of named animal species reproduce sexually.
SIMULTANEOUS HERMAPHRODITISM	Sexual systems in which the male and female sexes exist in the same individual simultaneously, i.e. a single individual produces both sperm and eggs at the same time.
SPERM	A mature male gamete which fertilizes the female gamete. It holds little to no cellular resources for the developing zygote and functions as a payload of genetic material. Because of this, the sperm is much smaller in volume than the female gamete and moves much faster. It is produced in far greater numbers because it requires far less resources to make.
STAMEN	The male reproductive organ of a flower that consists of a long-slender stalk called the filament along with an anther with sac-like structures that produce the pollen.
STRONG SOCIAL CONSTRUCTIONISM	In the sociology of sex, the idea that the two categories of male and female are wholly socially constructed and that there are no reliable criteria for consistently differentiating them. The sex spectrum's principles rely on this worldview.

TEMPERATURE SEX DETERMINATION	A unique mechanism for developing embryos into males or females, common in reptiles, where specific temperature values at which the eggs incubate trigger differentiation into a male or female, determining the sex of the embryo.
TESTIS	The male gonad responsible for the production and nursing of male germ cells into mature sperm. It regulates the hormonal system in males and is the main source of testosterone, which they produce at 15x more than females at any age.
TESTOSTERONE	The primary male sex hormone essential for the development of male genitalia as well as the promotion of secondary sex characteristics such as increased muscle and bone mass. It plays an important role in the physiology of both sexes but is substantially higher in males.
TRANSLOCATION	A genetic error during cell division where a piece of one chromosome breaks off and attaches to another chromosome. This can result in serious developmental disorders.
UTERUS	The organ in the mammalian female reproductive system where offspring develop and grow.
VAGINA	A muscular canal lined with nerves and mucus membranes that connects the uterus and cervix to the outside of the body, allowing menstruation, the reception of sperm into the female reproductive tract, and the delivery of offspring.

VAS DEFERENS	A coiled tube in the male internal reproductive system that carries sperm from the testes and into the ejaculatory duct.
VULVA	The external part of the female genitalia which includes the opening of the vagina, the labia majora, the labia minora, and the clitoris. The vulva provides protection to the internal parts of the reproductive system and plays a role in arousal and stimulation.
WOLFFIAN DUCTS	The primordial structure that develops into the male reproductive system (epididymis, vas deferens, seminal vesicle). The Wolffian duct develops in the presence of testicular testosterone and anti-Müllerian hormone and regresses in females.

ABOUT THE AUTHOR

Zachary Elliott is the founder of the Paradox Institute, a research group that specializes in teaching the biology of sex and sex differences to the public. Zach has been researching, reading, and writing about sex differences since 2017 and has written two other books on the subject—Sex Differences: A Land of Confusion and The Gender Paradox: Discrimination and Disparities in the Postmodern Era. He is also a writer and producer of more than twenty animated videos on the biology of sex, using his expertise in motion graphics and design to effectively communicate biological concepts.

Zach is also a black belt in Taekwondo and loves videography, video-editing, drumming, architecture and design, and many other creative passions. He lives with his partner, Cynthia, and is a proud father to his daughter.

Made in the USA
Middletown, DE
02 March 2024

50660399R00128